MW00789711

The Toolbox

Tools for Teaching Bikram Yoga

Teri Almquist

Teach From Love
North Andover, MA

Copyright Notice

Please do not copy, reproduce, distribute, or adapt this publication in any form, in any media, or by any means without the prior written consent of Teri Almquist.

© 2016 Teach From Love, All Rights Reserved.
Book design by Aram Designs, www.aramdesigns.com
Cover photograph by Liz Fairbanks, www.lizteal.com
Author photograph by Laurie McDonagh, www.lauriemcdonagh.com
All other photographs by Teri Almquist
Editing by Sam Sherman, Mary Kate Stein, and Steven Haver

First printing August 2016
Printed in North Andover, MA
ISBN 978-0-9975657-0-6
Library of Congress Control Number: 2016944269

Contact Information
Email: teri@teachfromlove.yoga
Teach From Love, Inc.
www.teachfromlove.yoga

Dedication

This book is dedicated to all the teachers who have stayed in my house and live in my heart—and to every student who has ever walked into a Bikram Yoga class.

Steven Haver and Diane Ducharme Gardner

Acknowledgments

Everyone we meet has something to teach us. There are so many people who have made this book a possibility, I can't begin to name them all. I am grateful to Bikram for the yoga practice that has changed my life and the lives of so many others. Thanks to the students and the community of teachers who inspire me to keep learning and growing.

Special thanks to my husband, Tom, who makes all things possible: You are a saint and the keeper of the yoga lyceum. To my daughters, Elaine and Bridget: Thanks for supporting me in finding myself. Thanks to my birth family and my yoga family. Thanks to Maryellen and the divas who give me a bit of perspective. And to Ben, Kat, and the Aussie crew, especially James, who started it all. Thanks to Mary Kate, Audrey, and Jill for your help. To Larry: Thank you for pulling it all together and making me cry (in a good way). To Liz, Ignacio, and Aram: I don't even have the words to tell you what a gift you have been to this project. You folks make me look good! To Sam, my genius: ¡Ole!

Special thanks to Diane, who taught me to practice and to teach: You taught me to love myself and Bikram Yoga. I can never thank you enough for sharing your vast wealth of knowledge with me. You embody what it means to teach from love.

Lastly, to Steven—my muse, inspiration, guide, writing partner, and friend: I couldn't have done any of this without you. Thank you.

Contents

"Every student deserves a good teacher, and every teacher deserves the opportunity to be a great teacher."

– Teri Almquist

Introduction
The Toolbox

I love mentoring teachers. After opening Bikram Yoga Merrimack Valley in North Andover, Massachusetts, in 2008, I also opened my home to teachers from around the globe who needed a place to teach, who wanted to learn more, and who had the desire to become the best teachers they could be. I have mentored hundreds of them, and I still love having teachers come work with me one-on-one. I have spent years sitting around my kitchen table with teachers who asked questions like:

"How do I learn to make corrections?"
"How do I help a student with an injury?"
"Why don't the new students do what I'm telling them?"
"Why do we lock the knee?"

Since graduating in 2005, I have been back to over a dozen teacher trainings. My goal at all of them is always the same: for students to have the best teachers. To that end I have focused on how to help teachers be the best they can be. The by-product of attending so many teacher trainings is that I have sat in on countless lectures and had the opportunity to learn from lots of teachers. I have been fortunate enough to collect great tools for teaching Bikram Yoga.

I am here to share those tools with you. Through years of mentoring, I have found there is a pattern to how teachers add tools to their toolboxes. There is a definite set of tools teachers need to go from being a good beginning teacher to a confident, knowledgeable teacher. It starts with building the foundation of Dialogue and then adding more tools over time. I've collected the tools you can use to be a great teacher in this book: from making corrections to dealing with the energy of the room, from understanding the Dialogue to using that knowledge to help students with injuries and limitations.

Teaching is not a linear task. You will go back over and over to work on your teaching tools, refining them as you grow. Growing in one area will lead you to grow in others. This book is a guide, a resource, a place to go when you feel stuck or bored (this is a sign new growth is coming).

The purpose of *The Toolbox* is to give teachers tools to teach their best class. I want you to take these tools and work on applying them in your teaching. I want you to collect lots more tools from lots of other teachers and find the ones to make you the best Bikram Yoga teacher you can be.

Chapter 1
Philosophy of Teaching

Teach from Love

My philosophy of teaching yoga is based on one simple idea: Love. All students will be loved until they love themselves, and then we will love them even more. So don't be scared as a student or a teacher.

> "Just breathe, everything else is optional."
>
> – Diane Ducharme Gardner

This tool of love is the most important one to hone. You became a Bikram Yoga teacher because you love this yoga and you want to share that love with others. This is the best place to start–this is the ground from where you build your class. When in doubt, go back to love. Teach from there. It won't always be easy, but it will be worth it. Love is where I start. When I don't know what to do for a student, I just try to figure out how to love them more.

By creating a loving space in class, I can invite anyone in. I keep my expectations simple and support students in the work they ultimately have to do for themselves. I can't do the yoga for them. However, I can give them space to be on their journey. I experience great joy from witnessing this journey. In the process, I have to be willing to take students as they come. They might be broken physically, mentally, and spiritually. Just as our hardest postures are always the ones we need the most, the challenging students are always the ones that need yoga the most.

Teach from love. No drama. When you go into the room, make a choice to love each student unconditionally. No judgments. Every student comes for his or her own reasons. This is their journey, we simply create the space for them to take it. It is never your class, it is always their practice.

Yoga Is Not about Yoga

The goal of a yoga practice is not to get better at yoga. The goal of the practice is to create a better life. That is the ultimate destination. To be a better you—to have a better understanding of who you are in your body, in your mind, in your spirit.

The postures are simple, a place to explore these relationships, to learn skills which translate outside the room to an improved quality of life. As Bikram Yoga teachers, we are trained to teach asana (postures). It is easy for us to focus on the depth of posture, and on the outcome of postures, as opposed to the outcome of practice based on technique.

In fact, the skills, technique, and attention to alignment are key to the depth of posture for students. But this is a side effect of the practice. The true measure of this practice is does it improve the quality of life outside the room?

The goal for all students is to have a better life outside the room. It doesn't matter what their postures look like, or what their attitude is like in the room. Are the tools, the skills, they are learning in the studio helping the students to have a better life when not in the room? (Teachers are students too; your practice should improve the quality of your life.)

I have spent time collecting tools to help in the healing process and so have you. I share these tools with the students to help them build the life they want, the life they desire and deserve.

The Foundation

The foundation for building a class is the Dialogue. I am a Dialogue teacher and happy about it. I am lucky enough to have learned what the words of the Dialogue mean and how they work with the body. I want to share that with you. Many teachers are hungry for this, especially new teachers. A major goal of this book is to help you learn what the Dialogue means and how it works. My philosophy is based on saying the Dialogue to facilitate the changes in the students. As you learn how it works—what it really means—you, too, will see how valuable this tool is. It is irreplaceable. You paid a lot of money for the tool, the Dialogue. Please use it. This book is a companion to your Dialogue.

The first step to being an effective teacher is you must know your Dialogue. Many teachers leave the Dialogue behind as a tool—they "move on" or "find their own voice." A common reason why they leave it is because they don't understand it or how it creates the interaction with the student—not really understanding the connection of the words with the body, the words with the meditation. To many teachers it might seem "not yoga enough" and they want to bring something else to the practice.

I want you to bring more than just the Dialogue to the practice. The tools you collect in your teaching toolbox can enable you to keep moving forward and growing as a teacher. I hope to create a bridge from your being able to say the Dialogue to your understanding how and why it works. To help you move beyond just reciting the words, to using those words to teach, inspire, and guide the students on their yoga journey.

Your goal as a teacher is to add more tools to your toolbox, starting with your foundation. When you really learn to use your Dialogue, you never have to think about building a foundation again. Then you add new tools, such as: making both basic and complex corrections; working with ill or injured students; teaching students with various learning styles; understanding knee issues, hip issues, back issues, and other physical limitations; teaching mentally ill, limited access, deaf, blind, and non-English-speaking students; and teaching pregnant students. More and more tools. You can always grow as a teacher. Growth as a teacher is infinite. You can always learn and add more skills to improve your teaching.

As you develop your teaching skills, add more tools to your toolbox, you gain confidence and realize you can help anyone. Never throw away one tool for the addition of another. Keep adding. The more tools you have, the better teacher you become because you have more to draw from. Later, you will have lots of tools to share, not only with your students, but with other teachers so they can grow, too.

Teaching from a place of love creates a positive relationship with each student in the room. Often teachers get stuck teaching from a place of fear. They fear they don't understand enough or that students will hurt themselves. Beginning students don't understand enough about the postures to hurt themselves, so again, don't be scared! Even if you don't understand everything in the Dialogue, it's okay to use it—it is designed to allow students to have all the information they need to be safe and get in and out of the postures effectively.

It's Simple

Bikram Yoga is simple. It's not always easy, but it is simple. Twenty-six postures and two breathing exercises in a hot room. The directions are simple: "feet together," "arms over your head," "palms together." Nothing fancy, yet incredibly effective. Simple skills broken down into basic steps. Due to its simplicity, the class is accessible to everybody, even if a student can only do the first step.

Life can be simple or complicated, and we make choices about this. This yoga practice is very simple. As a result, some teachers want to make it more complicated because it does not feel like enough; it is too simple. They may feel the Dialogue is lacking. Then teachers may feel they are not enough, or know enough, that they lack something. The truth is you have all the information you need; you just need time and guidance to understand it all.

Start with the simplicity of the practice, the skills, the directions, the Dialogue. The students who come in the room can be complicated, each one different, with different needs, and growing at different rates. This is the beauty of a yoga practice designed for everybody. Keep it simple.

Once you have a good foundation of Dialogue, you can keep growing as a teacher and learn to make corrections to students' practice. Lots of teachers are told "you're ready to make corrections" but are offered no real tools to help make those corrections. I want you to have tools to make effective, efficient corrections when the time comes, but first build a good foundation of Dialogue.

Discipline

The yoga practice (the same postures, same order, same directions, over and over) creates a moving meditation. A place of self-discovery and of self-discipline.
It is the job of the teacher to teach yoga; it is the job of the yoga to teach discipline.

It is easy for students who are struggling with themselves to turn the struggle into a battle between you and them. That's an easy battle to fight, and you as the teacher will lose—and ultimately the student loses as well. But let them struggle with themselves, and they will dig deep and find strength and determination they did not even know they had. Then they are truly on the journey of self-discovery through yoga. Don't try to dictate or give them the journey you think they should have. Give them space to learn, to grow, to self discover, and to make mistakes. Let them have their own journey within the discipline of the 26 & 2, and you will experience the joy of being on that journey with them. Celebrate their success; let go of their feelings of failure.

You have the road map, but the final destination is theirs. You have no idea where they are going, because you have no idea where they have been. Students arrive with their baggage and issues. They bring them in the room, and they get to decide what they leave behind, and what they take back with them. It is never your job to do it for them. Your job is to be supportive and read the road map (again and again).

I expect the teacher to be the most disciplined person in the room, to use the self-discipline honed in their personal practice to lead the class. It is never your job as the teacher to discipline the class or a student; it is to be self disciplined—to control yourself, your emotional state, and your emotional reactions. This is leading by example. If you have any personal struggle with your students, there is a place for you to work this out—on your own mat, not on the podium.

Rules for Teachers

- Stay on the podium
- Use the Dialogue to teach
- Don't touch students
- Clap quietly at Blowing in Firm
- Keep up a regular practice
- Don't date students

Rules

I believe having good boundaries is important for students' growth; that's why I have a lot of rules for my teachers. I have rules for teachers, but I have only one rule for students: Breathe. Breathing is mandatory, everything else is optional.

Students come in messy and disordered, and it might seem that having rules can give you—and them—a feeling of control. Don't worry—none of this is under your control. Rules often stand in the way of the learning process and growth (not just for the students, but for you as well).

Rules for Students

- Breathe

I love my students, and in loving them I want them to have a kind, safe environment in which to grow, to learn, to discover themselves. To create this space, I have tried to remove all the roadblocks to learning—anything that might stand in their way. To this end, I have removed all the rules that might hinder the learning process. Does this mean I don't care how students behave in the room? No, I care very much because I love them. I find there is no need to set up a list of rules to create a desired behavior. Instead I educate the students, give them tools to be successful in class.

Rules can create an adversarial relationship. They can become a way for the uncomfortable students to focus their discomfort outside themselves. Creating rules to be enforced by the teacher changes the dynamic of the struggle. Students can take their own struggle and transfer it into a struggle with the teacher, or worse, with another student in the room. The struggle for students should be with themselves. Their struggle, on their mats. How do you get rid of the struggle between the teacher and the students? Get rid of the rules.

Once there are rules, many teachers feel their job is to enforce the rules, and that can turn into a power struggle. The only struggle a student should have is with themselves on their mat. Rules that are designed to control students' behavior become the problem. Common rules some studios implement include: "Your only goal is to stay in the room." "Don't drink water in the first three postures." "Don't lie down during the standing series." "Drink water between postures only." "No sitting or lying down in the front row."

You can argue there are reasons for rules, and you could be right, but usually rules are about solving problems you don't have yet. If you teach with a lot of rules, it might be scary in the beginning to think about teaching with no rules. Don't be scared. Removing the rules opens up such great possibilities. The end result is so powerful and rewarding that you will end up wondering, as I do, what all the rules were for. Take away the rules, and teach from love.

A set of rules, a level of expectation, creates a homogeneous group of students, usually young healthy students—primarily women—with the strength and flexibility to do the postures. The students who really need the yoga—the stiff, injured, older, and out of shape—either don't come or don't come back because they feel they don't fit in. The goal is not to create a class where students need to fit in but to have a class where everyone feels they belong just as they are.

Philosophy of Teaching

Having rules about when students can drink water, or how to sit down, or certain behaviors in certain areas in the room, creates an attachment to other students' practice. Their struggle becomes focused on another student in the room, again taking their struggle off their mat. If the reason a student couldn't balance in Standing Bow pose is because another student drank water, or someone sat down or left the room and broke "the rule," you have created a whole new problem.

Perhaps you have been in a class where the teacher spends more time disciplining the students than teaching yoga. **It is the job of the teacher to teach yoga. It is the job of the yoga to teach discipline.**

Often, when teachers feel they don't know enough or that they lack the education and answers about the yoga, focusing on rules helps them to feel in control. However, as you learn more—as you add more tools to your toolbox—and become more confident in your teaching, then you will be able to lead your class confidently, without needing rules to create a desired effect. The yoga itself and your teaching will get the students to follow you.

When you don't have any rules and you open the door for anyone to come in, you create a space for students to figure things out, together, in cooperation with you. Instead of rules, create a platform to educate the students. They bring their issues, you bring your knowledge—in the process you all grow. Create a cooperative relationship with your students.

When a student's struggle is with themselves, they choose if they win or lose the battle (or their perception of winning or losing). If the student can transfer the battle with themselves to struggle with the teacher, they can win, the teacher can lose, and nothing is learned. Most times rules are a hindrance to growth for the teacher and the students. The point of no rules is that students grow and struggle on their own terms. While rules are thought to help, they usually hinder, slowing down the learning process. Rules can set students and teachers up for failure.

What we set up as rules are often just tools for good practice to be learned over time. Why does it bother you when students wipe sweat, drink water, lie down, or leave the room? Are you bothered because they are breaking the rule or because you know that it's better to do something else? Enforcing perpetuated rules is not teaching. What tools can you use to create a better learning experience for the students and ultimately a better teaching experience for you?

Right from the start, I aim to give the students tools to be successful and have a positive experience. At some studios, first-time students are told their only goal is to stay in the room and to sit down if they are dizzy or nauseous. In my studio, we avoid creating an expectation students will feel bad. We work to set students up for success, giving them tools to help them cope with the experience of a first class. The goal for the new student is to breathe and to have such a good experience that they want to come back tomorrow.

How do you get them to stay—especially when you think they want to run screaming from the room? Give them tools. When there is a new student in class, I start class by saying: "If you are uncomfortable,* sit down, even lie down, take a break, watch, join us when you're ready." I put some tools in their toolbox so they have skills to cope with the feelings they are experiencing.

It is great when new students stay in the room for the whole class. If they leave, cool down and dry off, the body has to adjust to the heat and humidity again when they come back in. However, if they do leave the room, students should feel they are welcome to come back in, they have not failed at the one goal set out for them. I want students to feel successful from the start.

Being allowed to rest, even encouraged to rest, is essential for beginners. Helping them to learn to control their heart rate is a powerful tool for them. For many beginners, what makes them want to run from the room is that their heart rate is up and they are uncomfortable. When you teach them from the start that they have control of their own body, their own decisions, and can make decisions to help themselves, they take their first step on the journey of self discovery.

Resting and sitting when they are uncomfortable allows students to stay in the room. When a student is resting, they are taking care of themselves. You might need to tell students to rest, to breathe through their nose, to teach them to take care of themselves. You might check in with a student who is resting to make sure the student is okay. If they are resting, then they are taking care of themselves. Your job is to teach yoga—so when a student is resting, don't give them a lot of attention. Teach the students who are doing the postures.

---

*"Uncomfortable": I have chosen that word carefully. Often teachers say, "if you are dizzy or nauseous, just sit down." How scary to be told you might feel bad or sick! Don't plant seeds you don't want to grow. "Uncomfortable" means different things to different people. I want students to start being in touch with how their body feels. If they rest before they feel terrible, the class is better, they have a better experience, and they want to come back. ✦

Giving students information and tools to cope with the situation is better than just enforcing a rule. Then they can start to make decisions for themselves. Think about the goal of giving them a better life outside the room. How do these tools transfer? It's okay to be uncomfortable, nothing bad happens. When you have no more coping skills, just breathe. If you need to rest, rest. In and out of the yoga room, these are tools to improve the quality of the students' lives.

Rules are designed to give teachers a sense of control. But none of this is under your control. When you let go of the need to control, teaching is fun and joyful.

> "Hell, there are no rules here—we're trying to accomplish something."
>
> – Thomas A. Edison

Many teachers think that without the rules there will be mayhem—students will go in and out of the room, students will be lying down all the time. But that's not true. Once you practice or teach in a studio with no rules, you'll see that there are more problems in the studios with rules. The rules allow the student to take their struggle off their mat. The rules create something to push back against.

Instead of saying "don't drink your water," educate your students about hydration. Instead of saying "don't lie down or sit down," teach them to take care of themselves, since that's what they're supposed to be doing. These are the skills that make life outside the room better.

If students spend time creating a mind/body connection and their body is telling them to sit down, but the rules prohibit it, why even bother to create the connection in the first place? If the goal is to have a mind/body connection and learn to take care of themselves, you must let them.

Let everyone in, let them stand in any row, let them fidget and wipe, be uncomfortable, struggle—then, you have the power to guide them, calm them, struggle with them, always in cooperation, never against them. Then, you will create a community of practitioners who inspire each other.

Always remember, this is not your class; this is their practice. Give them the gift of letting them learn about themselves while you keep it simple.

Drink Your Water

As Bikram Yoga teachers, we know the best situation is to be hydrated at all times, so the body is not looking for water during times of stress. But the reality is most students arrive under hydrated, then we put them in a hot room and create stress on the body. The human body has the most amazing ability to adapt to any environment, but usually that adaptation takes time.

In our community, there are many ideas about how much water to drink and when to drink it. It is best to educate the students to take care of themselves, especially when it comes to drinking water. My philosophy is simple: If you are thirsty, drink water. This also applies to teaching—take care of yourself. Talking dries out the mouth and vocal cords, so I encourage teachers to drink water while teaching.

At my studio, we don't talk about drinking water. At party time, the teacher tells the students that this is the only water break we take together, and for the rest of class, if they are thirsty, drink water. Neither the teachers nor the students think about it again. We don't notice if, or when, the students are having water or not— no one notices, because no one is attached to what other students are doing in class. Each student is focused on their own practice.

Talking about or creating arbitrary rules about drinking water in class creates an attachment to water. It creates an environment where students are attached to who is drinking water and who is not. Some teachers don't want the students to be "attached" to drinking water (the concept of non-attachment), but what creates the non-attached relationship? If it's because it's a rule or the teacher said so, what have the students learned? If students come to understand on their own that drinking lots of water throughout the day is better than drinking a lot of water during class, then they have had a real growth experience.

Trust that the adults who come to class know when they are thirsty. They might not be thirsty and are drinking because they are overwhelmed or uncomfortable, but it's best to understand that if they think they need water, they need water. Give the students tools to be successful, tell them to take care of themselves. Trust them to follow through on this process. If a student is drinking water before party time, ignore it. If they drink water while other students are in a posture, ignore that too. Create a loving space for the students, give them information and let them learn how to listen to their own body. (Now drink some water).

Look in the Mirror

Bikram was once asked why we need mirrors in the room. His answer: "It's not enough for you to suffer, you have to see yourself suffer." Sounds like another part of the torture chamber—to see yourself suffer. But think about this idea: What happens when people see suffering? For most people, it creates a response called "compassion." It's not enough to be compassionate with others, you must be compassionate with yourself. Not always an easy task.

Many students (new and old) have a hard time looking in the mirror. They might not like what they see. The self talk connected with seeing oneself is not always kind. "Why is my nose so big?" "I need to lose weight." "She can do it, I can't." "My thighs are fat." "When did I get so bald?" "How can I lose this stomach?" Students need to be encouraged to look in the mirror over and over.

Instructing students to look into their "own eyes" can make it harder. After a lot of yoga, students work through their issues and it usually gets easier. Until then, it might be difficult for students to look at themselves. Some students might see everything wrong and none of what's right. Be patient with them, remind them to look in the mirror.

When we tell them, "Concentrate one point on your left knee in the mirror," or "focus one point on your right foot in the mirror" it helps them to start looking at their own body. This starts to create the mind/body connection and hopefully, over time, students can look at themselves and see how wonderful they are.

Students should also use the mirror to help align their own body—as you teach with Dialogue. The mirror is a tool for alignment, to help make the mind/body connection. It can also be a great tool for you (as the teacher) to look at the bodies. Sometimes by changing the perspective, how you are looking at the student, you see them differently. You can see where their alignment is off. While standing on the podium, you can use the mirror to help you see the room and your students.

The Ten Thousand Dollar Book

My philosophy is simple: Teach from love. I want you to start filling your teaching toolbox, then you can teach from love, too. Starting with the Dialogue—use it, learn to apply it as an effective tool, let it be the basic foundation of your class.

Some teachers can be effective without Dialogue. There was a time before the standardized Dialogue when teachers were trained by Bikram. He spent many hours teaching them how the body works with the postures. One of my goals is to bridge the gap between the Dialogue and this understanding of the postures, so you can have both tools and be a highly effective, confident teacher while using the Dialogue.

The Dialogue—what it means in relationship to the body, the physiological effects of the practice as well as the psychological effects—can take many years of teaching to understand. There are new things to learn all the time. The longer I have been teaching, the more I go back to the Dialogue for answers to my teaching questions and the more I realize how little I understand. The more time you spend teaching, the more you will want to refer to the Dialogue for answers to your teaching questions.

> "Having doesn't mean anything if you don't know how to use it."
>
> – Bikram Choudhury

It may be frustrating when Bikram answers a question about a posture by saying, "What does my Dialogue say?" But he is giving you the answer. The answers are in the Dialogue. You have to go back, over and over, and read it, look at it, search for the answers. You won't have access to Bikram to ask questions after class, but you will have his Dialogue to find the answers you need.

Chapter 2
The Dialogue

Building Your Foundation

If love is the ground on which we build our class, the Dialogue is the foundation we lay on that ground. It is the set of tools from training that you need for every class you teach. That is why you must know the Dialogue.

You spent nine weeks at teacher training to learn specific skills. The first goal at training is for you to memorize the Dialogue. The simple set of directions will lead a student in and out of the postures safely, effectively, and efficiently. This is all the information the student needs to try the posture. The Dialogue has all the directions you need to teach them as a new teacher.

> "It's important that you know the most powerful kind of honesty there is. And that is always being careful to teach this knowledge of yoga—this oh so powerful worldview—exactly as you have learned it."
>
> – Geshe Michael Roach and Christie McNally
> *How Yoga Works**

First, you have to know the Dialogue. Nine weeks of training is the time it takes to get certain skills—tools into your toolbox. At this point, you should have figured out a way to memorize. You should also

---

*I highly recommend you read the book *How Yoga Works*. ✐

be able to get this information to come back out of your mouth—a way to recall and deliver the information. This is what you practiced in posture clinic. Most likely, you are fine standing in front of the class and saying the words of the Dialogue. These are the skills that continue to serve you through all the years of teaching.

For your first few classes, it is an exercise in standing up and saying the Dialogue. In the beginning, you work on repeating the directions, over and over again. Of course there is more to teaching; however, until you build a solid foundation, it is difficult to add more tools and still teach a precise, effective class.

The Dialogue is what makes this yoga unique and makes it work. This is a healing yoga designed to have therapeutic benefits for all students who seek to heal themselves through the hard work you inspire them to do. You must continually go back—especially in the first months and years of teaching, and make sure you are working on proper Dialogue.

The main reason to use the Dialogue is because it works. It's a very succinct, clear set of directions. It is, for the most part, unambiguous: "Arms over your head sideways," "right foot step to the right." It uses simple, neutral language. While the grammar can be odd in places, the longer you teach using the Dialogue, the more you realize how well it works, how these strange constructs of language make students listen differently. So just say it, even if you don't understand all the reasons why you are giving them these directions, even if they don't make sense to you yet. Just keep saying them over and over. Over time you will see how these words affect the students' practice. When your Dialogue is precise, the students' practice is more precise.

As a new teacher, you might not think the Dialogue works. You might be in the front of the room saying the words, but the students don't seem to be getting it. You wonder if giving the students instructions in your own words would help them understand it better. Perhaps you think you are saying the Dialogue, but actually you are saying some of the Dialogue, but you are missing information. It's not that the Dialogue doesn't work, you just don't have all of the Dialogue you need yet, or perhaps your sequencing is off. In other words, you have the directions slightly out of order.

If you change the Dialogue—even if the change seems small or inconsequential—you might change it in a way that prevents a student from being able to heal. The yoga works, as prescribed, as written. Don't take away a student's right to heal themselves physically, emotionally, and spiritually. Even if you don't understand something in the Dialogue, know it is there for a reason.

Just as we don't explain all the reasons for the steps of a posture, the students trust us; trust that the Dialogue has all the directions for a reason. You can learn all the reasons for what we say over time, but if you stop saying it, you won't. Watch how what you say affects the bodies in the room, but never take anything away or you might take something from the students that they need.

Same Words, Same Skills

When a studio is Dialogue-based, each teacher gives the same basic directions. Each student learns over time, according to their own needs, pace, and readiness—physically, mentally, and emotionally. We can all think of a time when we learned something new in class: a new direction, or a new line of Dialogue, but the truth is the teachers said that line in every class we were in. You heard it when you were ready to integrate it. By hearing the Dialogue, each individual student has time to grow at their own pace. Students who have been practicing for years can stand next to a brand new student and they both have access to the information they need.

Students learn in different ways. Some learn by listening, some learn by watching, and some learn by doing. The Dialogue and the class structure make our class accessible to all. Students hear the directions step by step, they can watch the more experienced students in the room, and the postures are the same each time, making the class work for a variety of learning styles. Using the Dialogue, we are continually reinforcing a series of skills, a series of simple movements. Through the class, we use the same words for the same skills over and over. Students learn the skill and then reapply the skill in other postures. Often, we use the same skill and similar words with slightly new information. By using this same skill, same words, it becomes easier for students to be successful. The students, without even realizing it, learn quickly, regardless of learning style.

All the teachers teaching the same skill with the same words is important to the practice. We don't teach our students postures, we teach individual skills which they reapply. Students don't have to master the whole posture, they just have to do all the skills they are able to do.

Teachers teaching the same way means students should not care who is teaching. Every teacher has something to teach us. It's normal that some teachers resonate more with us than others. The teachers who challenge us probably have more to teach us than the ones for which we have an affinity. By use of Dialogue, all teachers teach from the same place, helping students practice non-attachment.

When memorizing the Dialogue, as you move from posture to posture, you might find it gets easier to learn the words, the directions to the postures. The Dialogue is designed to use simple directions for a skill. "Arms over your head sideways." You say it the same way in all the postures that use that skill. Once students learn a skill, they don't have to learn it again. They just reimplement it. "Right leg step to the right." You use the same words with a little variation in postures, but the same skill.

By using the Dialogue, you have already taught the students most of the skills needed to do the postures. Even a beginner can do it, because this style of teaching lends itself to teaching everyone. For example, Rabbit pose uses skills repeated from other postures.

Once students have learned the basic skills to do the posture, the repetitive nature of the practice—hearing the same words over and over—allows students to quiet their minds. Over time this creates the moving meditation. The use of Dialogue is what eventually facilitates the moving meditation for students.

Skill Variations

We use the same words to teach the same skill in different postures. Sometimes the instructions vary slightly to apply a skill in a new way. For example, the same skill can be used with a different body part:

Standing Head to Knee:
"Evenly distribute the weight all over the right foot, equally, the same."

Cobra:
"Distribute the body weight all over the hands-palms, equally, the same."

Or change the orientation of the body slightly:

Tree:
"Heel touching the costume. Sole of the foot is facing the ceiling."

Head to Knee:
"Heel should touch the costume. Create pressure with the left foot sole against the right leg biceps of the thigh muscle."

The directions of the Dialogue are like a road map—a set of commands, what to do, how to do it and the effect of doing it. Clear and simple. You can think of the Dialogue as speaking directly to the body. The teacher is talking to the right leg, the arms, the body, telling each part what to do. There is a lot of information in the Dialogue, but none of it is complex. The heat, the room, lights, the mirror, a teacher with a microphone talking non-stop—many beginners can find this overwhelming at first. This means they have to focus on the task at hand—what to do.

Moving Meditation

Skills for Rabbit Pose

Skills taught throughout the series are reused in different postures. Rabbit pose is a good example of how the student applies skills already learned in other postures.

- Sit down "Japanese style"
- Towel over the heels
  (this is the only new skill)
- Grab heels
- Pull heels
- Tuck chin to chest
- Forehead on knees
- Head on floor
- Roll forward
- Elbows straight

Concentrating for 90 minutes can be a challenge for most students, especially if they are new to Bikram Yoga. The class is designed so they have no choice; they must focus on what they are doing. It is difficult to let other thoughts from outside come in. In the struggle to move the body, the mind starts to quiet. Maybe not quiet at first, but focused mostly on what they are doing in the moment. Yes, the new students are looking around, drinking water, wiping off sweat. To teachers this looks like they are unfocused, distracted. But the distractions are actually focused on what they are doing in the moment—what's happening right now. These "distractions" are dealing with the discomfort in the moment, this is the journey the students take to a true yoga practice, as a spiritual practice.

As students listen to the same words, make the same moves, do the same postures in the same order, over time the mind quiets to more easily focus on what the body is doing in the current moment. This becomes the mantra which leads the moving meditation, allowing a student to come into class and move the body while quieting the mind. This is what a yoga practice is, the healing of the body through asana—the ability to quiet the mind.

The moving meditation is one of the powerful parts of the Dialogue practice. As you grow as a teacher and become more confident in what you know, the Dialogue actually works better. It is important to understand what to share with your students. When teachers deviate from the Dialogue—start explaining, using their own words, demonstrating—it can make the students start to think, taking them out of their meditation. The goal of the practice is to quiet the mind while moving the body through the series of postures. This means students don't have to think for 90 minutes. Teach with knowledge and confidence, but let the students have their moving meditation.

The use of the Dialogue with its consistent and repetitive nature will keep the students connected with you not just physically, but mentally. It will keep their minds present in the room and connected to the yoga practice. It keeps them in the moment. As students deepen their practice, the words—the chant, the mantra, the Dialogue—allow them to quiet the mind. We are speaking to the body, but the mind stays quiet. The students learn to quiet the mind while they work in the body. Over time, the students will develop a connection with their spiritual self.

There is no dogma attached to Bikram Yoga. The students' spiritual journey is their own. It's not up to us to decide what that journey is. The Dialogue is the tool to quiet the mind, opening space for the students to connect with themselves. The Dialogue allows for this powerful combination of physical movement and meditation. This is a gift you give your students by using the Dialogue.

It's rewarding when you understand what you are teaching and you can comfortably answer questions students have—when you are the place they go to ask the questions because they trust you. However, don't interfere with the meditation of the class. Just like learning not to overload the room energetically, you don't want to overload students with information they don't need or can't access. Consistent Dialogue is what will help the students to improve their practice.

Teach Every Body

The Dialogue is designed to work with all bodies. Strong, inflexible, flexible, not strong, injured or healthy. As teachers, we have a tendency to teach to our own bodies, from our own practice. For many (but not all) teachers, this is a flexible body. The concern is when you can only teach bodies like your own.

To be an effective teacher, you must relate to all body types, and the Dialogue is designed to do that. While it's important not to teach only from your own practice, bringing that knowledge into the room is a tool you can share with students with similar bodies to your own. There are some bodies like yours and your experience can help them. It's normal that we see the practice through our own filters, our own bodies, but the Dialogue allows you to teach to all bodies, even those very different from your own. This is the beauty of this practice and the Dialogue.

For the flexible body, the Dialogue can help build strength. The strong body can use its strength to create flexibility. The use of precise, clear Dialogue helps to create strength and flexibility, as well as a balance of the two. For strong bodies, the leverage of the postures uses the student's strength to create more flexibility. For the flexible body, the controlled movements develop strength. Because there is a tendency to teach to bodies like our own, the flexible teacher might focus on flexibility. It is easy to see improvements to flexibility and depth of the postures.

Many teachers have been taught by instructors who don't use or don't understand the Dialogue or how it works with all bodies. The focus is on depth of postures, the result that is easy to see. In turn, flexible students become "successful" in class and are encouraged to go to teacher training. It's common that we as teachers can look at flexible students and give them ways to be more flexible, but that's not what they need. When you give students the gift of the Dialogue, they can access in the body what they need more of, what they currently lack. The Dialogue is designed to fill in the missing gaps in the body to help create a balance of strength and flexibility.

Sequencing

The philosophy of "Try the Right Way" is an important part of our class. The sequence is the step-by-step way to try the right way. Step A, then B, then C. As the teacher, if your sequencing is off, you can't help the student get to their full range of motion. The sequence of the postures is detailed in the Dialogue. The sequencing becomes even more important when you start teaching students with limited mobility, with injuries, or just inflexible bodies.

Often, teachers who find themselves saying "stay with my words," do not have proper sequencing. If you have trouble keeping students with you, look at your sequencing. Understanding the sequencing will allow you to teach students with limitations. You will understand where postures start and end, so you can help them get through the posture to the best of their ability.

What to Do

Telling students what to do can sometimes be uncomfortable, but that's your job. The Dialogue is written as a series of commands; most of these commands are talking to the body. Some teachers begin to use descriptive language instead of the commands of the Dialogue. Teachers take away their own power when they start to describe the body as opposed to telling the body what to do. It's okay to be powerful.

The students need you to tell them what to do. Descriptive language takes them out of their meditation. Talking directly to the body allows the mind to quiet, allowing for meditation. Descriptive language can also reinforce bad technique. For example, saying, "Your elbows are locked" makes students think their elbows are locked even when they aren't (because you just said so).

Using Commands

Remember to give directions rather than descriptions. Avoid descriptive phrases that include words like: is, are, you want to.

DO command	DON'T describe
Lock your knee.	Your knee **is** locked.
Bend your spine backward from coccyx to the neck.	Your back **is** bending.
Elbows locked, arms always touching with your ears.	Your elbows **are** locked. Your arms **are** touching with your ears.
Sit down between the heels.	**You want to** sit down between your heels.

It can be difficult to hear yourself describing instead of giving commands while teaching. This is a good reason to record yourself and listen to your class, or have other teachers take your class and give you feedback.

Push and Play

The Dialogue provides you with the space in your class to help students through the use of corrections. When you know you can easily deliver the Dialogue, and no longer have to think about what you are saying, I call this "Push and Play."* When you can stand on the podium, start class, and not think about what you're saying

---

*You might be a Push and Play teacher (that is, not thinking about what you're saying) and not using Dialogue. If so, be patient with yourself when you go back to learn Dialogue. What you say is so automatic. It can take some time to undo. Give yourself the time to rebuild your foundation. 🔧

for 90 minutes, then your mind can create space to see, really see, what individual students need in the way of technique to improve their practice. Eventually you will start looking for these corrections.

In the long run, being able to use, say, and implement the Dialogue will take you from being a good beginning teacher to a great teacher. But without the good foundation, it's hard to add in more tools. Take time to build a good foundation; don't be in a hurry. Keep working with the tool you paid so much money for and gave so much time to at training. Continue to give it as much time as needed.

It takes at least six months (100 or more classes) and perhaps even longer until your Dialogue is consistent and you are giving the students clear, step-by-step commands to be in the posture (Push and Play). You might be thinking, "Is that all there is? I paid all that money to say the same thing over and over? How boring!" Great, you are exactly where you need to be. Welcome to being a beginning teacher!

This boredom is just a sign that you are ready for a next step. You are ready to put new tools in your toolbox. You are ready to work on correcting students' technique. The Dialogue is the tool that you are going to use to make the corrections. If you haven't mastered that tool yet, you cannot move on to corrections. You will always continue to work on your Dialogue, even as you move on to other teaching skills.

Chapter 3
Making Corrections

"The Slower You Do Is Better"

Once you have been teaching a while, you might be told to start making corrections. As teachers, corrections are really what we do–that is the true experience of teaching. However, often new teachers are not told how to make corrections or what to correct.

I believe many teachers are told to start making corrections too soon. Make sure your foundation is solid before you start making corrections. The Dialogue is the foundation of your class. It is the tool that enables you to take all these other steps forward. Review your Dialogue over and over–throughout your career as a teacher.

When you have built a solid foundation, you have

"How do we know in a given situation what would benefit somebody? How do we know that we're not just being big egotists and intruding when we aren't needed? The more I think about it, the more complicated it is. It's like a trap door opens and you get led to the really deep spiritual questions."

– George Saunders

the Dialogue down, you are no longer thinking about what to tell the students in each posture, you can manage the room (heat and humidity), and your class just flows, then you can start thinking about making corrections.

You might have a lot going on in the room before you can even start to see the students. It takes time to really see and understand how the students' bodies work in relationship with the Dialogue. That's okay. Give yourself time to build a foundation.

Having It

When Dialogue and the room are second nature, and you can operate in Push and Play mode, you are finally at a point where you can start making efficient and effective corrections. As a new teacher, you need to take care of the students and solve any problems that arise (such as the new student who doesn't have a mat or water). Otherwise, you can let a lot of things slide in the beginning and focus on building a good foundation, learning to see what students are doing.

You have to learn to observe students' technique from the front of the room. If you take the time to do this, you will be able to see everything that is happening in the students' bodies from the front of the room. You don't need to move to the back or the side to see the grips. You are going to see that the grip is wrong by observing the body from the podium. Give yourself time to do this. It takes time to learn to see from the front of the room—all the bodies, the whole room.

Once you know your Dialogue well, the first tools for making corrections are simple. The first step is simply to learn to see what you want to correct for a while. Learn to observe the students from the front of the room. Keep saying your Dialogue while you learn to look at the students and start to see what they are doing well, how the Dialogue works with the body. You might start to see things you want to "fix." Keep in mind, when we make "corrections," there is nothing wrong with the student. We are not fixing the students, we are just correcting their asana technique.

The second step is **don't touch**—no physical corrections. While it might seem easy to correct this way, it sends the students and you in the wrong direction. At first, a challenging part of making good verbal corrections is figuring out what to say and how to say it, so this is a whole collection of tools to add to your toolbox.

When you first learn to leave your Dialogue to make a correction, you might get tripped up trying to go back. That's normal. The technique takes some practice. One way to practice is through praising a student. Say a name, tell them "that was good" or "nice job," then go back to the Dialogue. Be sure not to just praise students who have achieved depth of posture, but also the student who backed off to help themselves or integrated a new skill (for example, being able to balance on one foot in Standing Head to Knee pose, or to grab their heels for the first time in Camel pose). This builds confidence in the student, which is one of the main things we do as yoga teachers.

Give All the Directions

Sometimes you want to correct things preemptively, before you've gotten to the direction in the Dialogue. Make sure to give all the directions before correcting. For example, in Cobra pose: "Come up halfway only…" Many teachers want to correct the new student who comes up all the way, elbows straight. But wait. Keep saying the Dialogue and watch them self correct when they hear "…until only your belly button is touching the floor. The rest of your upper body is in the air. At the same time, from the side, your elbows should be 'L', 90° degree angle, like a rectangle." Say all the Dialogue before you correct the student. Once they hear all the directions, often they make the correction on their own.

What Do You See?

You will see things you want to correct. Keep in mind that you don't have to correct everything you see. You can learn to pick and choose what to correct. Scan the bodies and watch how the bodies respond to the Dialogue—what you are saying. This will help you see what you need to correct and when to give a student time to learn.

As you talk about various body parts in the posture, scan the room and look at the parts of the body—the hips or arms or knees. Teach yourself to see the corrections, then you can start to look for corrections based on understanding the technique of each posture and the students' bodies.

When you're teaching a posture, scan the room for the thing that looks different. For example, when you say "feet together," you don't have to look at everyone's feet to make sure they're together, just scan the room to find the thing that looks different and look at those feet. Perhaps some students have knocked knees or bunions preventing them from bringing their feet together. A student might look different for a reason. You have to see it and recognize what you're seeing. If there is no apparent reason why a student's feet are apart, then the correction is "Bob, feet together." Over time, you train your brain to look for the thing (the alignment) that is different. The more you practice this skill, the easier it is. Keep trying. In the beginning, it is enough to see the differences in the bodies.

How to Use It

When you see something you want to correct—don't! Wait. Say nothing. It will help you remember that you wanted to make a correction. Put it in your memory and after you finish class, open the Dialogue and read that posture. What was the line, the direction, that could have helped the student? Look at the Dialogue. There is most likely a line that can improve their technique. Did you miss a line during your class? Is that direction part of your consistent dialogue? If it's not, it's time to add it back in. Don't forget to read the additional Dialogue and the left sides (second sets) as there might be a line there to make the correction.

If you find some additional Dialogue to use, now is the time to add it to your repertoire. Often new teachers are told to "mix it up" or "say different things" on each side of each set of a posture. The left side and additional Dialogue is the tool you need to get there. This will add more information to your dialogue and add skills to improve the students' practice.

Corrections ideally should be from the Dialogue. There are many reasons for this. Using the Dialogue to correct reiterates a skill the student might already have, or gives them a skill they need to have. We all teach the same skills with the same words, so if the student either does not understand, or is unable to integrate the skill yet, it will be repeated in every class so they can get it at another time. Also, it gives them the ability to self correct in another class.

Students remember the correction you gave them and when another teacher uses the same line of Dialogue, the student can recall and reintegrate the correction. Often by fixing a skill in one posture, when the skill is repeated in another posture, the student can self correct again. We don't end up correcting the same student over and over for the same skill because the words help them make the correction. (You will correct some students over and over, and that's okay.) Remember, the whole class hears you and often tries to implement the corrections. Give the gift of good corrections.

Correct Technique

Corrections should be positive and technique-based. Positive corrections focus on what you want the students to do. If you are correcting by saying "don't," you may need to go back to the Dialogue. Make sure you have all the information about what to do, how to do it, and the effect (result) of doing it. When you find you are correcting students by telling them what not to do ("don't"), try to change it to a positive ("do"). For example: instead of "don't bend your elbows," say "elbows locked." Instead of "don't wipe, scratch, readjust," say "hold still, relax, breathe." Remember to plant only seeds you want to grow. Tell them what you want them to do.

Correct the Action, Not the Result

Understanding the technique allows you to correct the action instead of the result. The actions—what to do—are in the directions of the Dialogue.

Backward Bending:
"Arms back immediately, try to touch the wall behind you." When students (especially inflexible students) hear the correction "chest up," they come out of the backbend. "Arms back" increases benefit and gets the desired result for all students, flexible and inflexible. The result of stretching back is that the chest does comes up, opens more.

Standing Separate Leg Head to Knee:
"Bring maximum weight on the front leg, so your right side hip is sticking up towards the ceiling, to get your both hips in one line." The action is to bring the weight forward, and the hip coming up is a result of this action.

Cobra:
"Stretch your elbows down toward the hips ... to bring your shoulders down." Stretching the elbows down is the action. The shoulders coming down is the result.

Technique-based corrections focus on telling the students what action to take to get the desired result. Look at what to do: this is the correction. It is often easy to see the result; a common mistake teachers make is teaching the result of the posture instead of teaching the action. Often result-based corrections focus on depth of posture; however, what students need are tools to create that depth—the action. If all you have to correct in a posture is the depth, you need to go back to the Dialogue and find the tool you can give them to improve their technique.

How to Make Corrections

There are different ways to correct students. One of the most effective ways is to use a student's name and a line of Dialogue. Because you are using Dialogue to correct, it is applicable to all the students. Sometimes you can simply look at the student and say the correction.

The two types of corrections are individual corrections and global corrections. Both can be made with lines of Dialogue (ideal) or without (helpful at times). When making an individual correction, I use the student's name. This correction is meant for that student, but keep in mind that all students in the room also hear this correction. For example: "Push your right hip forward. Susie, push your left hip forward." An individual correction is when you leave the straight series of directions, the Dialogue, to help a student fix technique that is off.

A global correction is a general correction given to the whole room. It can be directed at one or two students, but for whatever reason you give the information to the whole class. Remember, you're trying to create a teamwork approach, not an adversarial relationship, and global corrections can help. Sometimes they are just a great teaching moment for everyone. For example, in between sets of Standing Head to Knee or Standing Bow Pulling pose, I might remind students to look in the mirror by saying "You have been balancing your whole life with your head up, so look in the mirror." It's really aimed at a student who is looking at the floor, but all students hear it and can use it.

Hit and Run

"Hit and Run" is a correction technique you can use to create non-attachment in your teaching. When you first start making corrections, give students the necessary information to correct their technique, then move on. Even if they don't make the correction, don't be attached to the outcome of the correction. The basic idea is simple: give the correction, look at the student when you start saying the correction, and by the time you finish the correction, be looking at someone else. You can look back at some point to see if the correction was implemented, but if you are not looking at them, it is easier to let go of the outcome.

It's okay if they don't get it today, or the correction was not effective today. Come back tomorrow, we are going to do it again. We teach the same postures in the same order using the same directions. The only thing that changes is the student. They are different every day, and you get to celebrate their changes and successes. But let go of their struggle to make those changes.

We all want our students to succeed—that's normal, it's part of the reason we became teachers. Remember, the struggle is where students' success lies. Don't be attached to what they can and can't do. They need to struggle on several levels—physically, emotionally, and spiritually. Let them. This is how they will grow.

Don't Hump the Newbies, Don't Poke the Crazies

New students are the easiest to correct because they come with no skills to do the postures. You could correct everything. Please don't! Don't hump the newbies. Mostly, the new student needs to hear the Dialogue over and over (several times, first and second set, left and right sides, same directions, over and over) to understand the skills.

There are a few reasons to correct new students. The new student may need to be reminded to breathe and how to breathe (normally, in and out through the nose). You need to watch their breathing. Are they panting or holding their breath? When a student is not breathing properly, they might start to panic or the body might try to reset their breathing (by passing out). With new students, watch that they keep breathing normally, even if they have to sit down or lie down. Standing in the front of the room allows you to see this. You can't monitor students breathing from the back of the room.

Teach them from the start that they need to take care of themselves and give them tools to do that. I tell new students that if they are uncomfortable, to sit down or lie down, take a break, and join us when ready. The expectation is they will learn first to take care of themselves. I don't tell students that their goal is to stay in the room—the goal is to take care of themselves. Give them a set of tools to do that (sit down, lie down, breathe through the nose).

If a student becomes overwhelmed and their first response is to leave, remind them of the tools they already have to deal with the situation. If they implement these tools and they look okay, then they can leave—go get some air and come back in when they are ready. If a student looks rough, I try to get them to stay—explaining I want to watch them to make sure they are okay, so just lie down.

The common mistakes made by beginners (grips, feet together, etc.) are skills they have time to learn, so use corrections judiciously. If you decide to correct new students, be careful not to overwhelm them. It's okay to let them do it wrong. It's okay to not correct them. Let them struggle—in the struggle is where they find their success. It's not only okay to let them struggle, it's your job. There are many reasons **not** to correct a student; being new to the practice is a good reason.

This is a healing yoga, not just physically but emotionally. Often people looking to heal will come to yoga. We try to accommodate everyone who wants to come to class. There are students who come to class with stability issues. With most stable students, we can gauge the range of responses to certain interactions. Unstable students may react in inappropriate or unpredictable ways. It's always best when dealing with these individuals to limit the personal interaction in class. Over time, you might create a relationship with this student that allows you to better predict their reactions, but until then: don't poke!

The nice thing is most of these students give you clear cues of their instability. In my experience, giving a global correction or explaining between the postures is a way to help students who cannot handle individual corrections and might have an inappropriate response. Students who are just uncomfortable with their name being used for corrections should be educated about our verbal correction style.

Types of Learners

In every class you will have students with various learning styles. Being familiar with the different learning styles will help you gear your corrections to each student in the way that they learn most effectively. Learning styles are generally separated into three basic groups: auditory, visual, and kinesthetic. Most students are not just one type of learner. They might have a more dominant style, but they combine different styles to help them learn. You might be able to identify different learners in class; you can often identify which type of learner a new student is by watching their Pranayama Breathing.

Auditory Learners

Auditory learners can access information best by listening. For these students, the Dialogue is an effective way to teach them. They hear the directions and can use them to try to do the posture one step at a time.

Auditory learners might not be doing Pranayama Breathing properly; however, it looks good in the first one or two breaths. Teach them with simple, complete directions—use the Dialogue. This class is perfect for the Auditory learner. They can usually follow along well from the beginning. When you make a simple verbal correction, they get it. They look at the teacher to see what you are saying. Smile at them! They can hear the difference in different teachers' Dialogue. It's important that all the teachers are consistent, class to class, as this allows the auditory learners to trust us. They will try to implement any correction they hear—even one for someone else.

Visual Learners

Visual learners need to look at the other students to see what to do. This type of student looks at you while you teach and also looks around the room. They need to watch the more experienced students before they attempt the posture.

During Pranayama Breathing, Visual learners might appear to be a step behind as they need to wait to see what others are doing before they can do it themselves. Telling these students to focus on themselves in the mirror doesn't give them the tools they need to be successful. They need to watch the other students to figure out what to do. Visual learners might not drop their heads back right away during breathing or back bending postures because they want to see what the other students are doing first. Once they get the hang of the posture then they are fine. Between the first and second sets, you can remind these students it's okay to watch. For these students, you can also do a visual representation* to correct. Don't overwhelm them with too much verbal correction; it's not always accessible to them.

---

*A visual representation is a way of showing a technique or element of a posture. For example, in the setup for Awkward pose, you can show students the six-inch gap with your hands as you say the Dialogue (then they can actually see it). A visual representation is different from demonstrating. Demonstrating is unnecessary, because the new student can see the more experienced students' postures. Demonstrating also interrupts the flow of the class. ✒

Kinesthetic Learners

Kinesthetic learners learn by doing. These students require time to try over and over to integrate the information into their own bodies. Doing the same thing repeatedly, with the same directions, helps them learn the postures. Kinesthetic learners are often the hardest students to teach as beginners. They can look like they don't understand what they are doing or what you are saying. They appear lost, and they need more time to develop as a student. They usually already have a good mind/body connection. Often teachers want to vary what they are saying, thinking it will help this type of learner, but that just delays the process. This student, all students, derive great benefit from the repetitive nature of the practice. The repetition does not bore the students, it makes it easier for them.

If these students struggle with Pranayama Breathing, I might try to put them at ease by saying, "Don't worry, this is the only thing we do that takes any coordination," before moving on to Half Moon pose. Help Kinesthetic learners deal with frustration by praising them.* This is true of all students, but helping this type of learner with frustration is particularly important to keeping them practicing.

There is a period of time needed for this learner to grasp the postures. You can't rush this process. The only thing you can do is give them time to understand the posture. They need to be told that we do the same postures in the same order in every single class. They have time to get it. Tell them when they are doing something right. If they get a skill right in a posture, then they can apply that same skill again in other postures. Focus first on the things they can easily do.

To sum up, knowing how a student best integrates information can help you formulate corrections in a way that is most easily accessible to them: short description for the Auditory learners; a quick visual cue for the Visual learners; and space and time for the Kinesthetic learners to figure it out in their own body.

Students Lacking a Mind/Body Connection

While you might be able to identify specific types of learners, be aware that students who lack a mind/body connection might look like a Kinesthetic learner. They may or may not be. This lack of connection is especially true of students

---

*Be mindful when praising a Kinesthetic learner. Using phrases like "perfect" or "that's right" when that is not the case will slow down their learning process. Instead, use terms like "that's better" or "good enough for today" to help reinforce that they are moving in the right direction. ✐

who have suffered abuse or trauma. The technique to help this student is the same: patience. Give them time to create the connection between their body and mind as well as connection to the skills you are teaching them. Stay off their mat, literally and figuratively.

Don't Touch the Students

Over time, the training of teachers has changed. Prior to a formal training, Bikram would choose a student who had been practicing for a while and give them verbal directions to adjust another student in class. Physical corrections were given as a way to train the potential new teacher about the body, not necessarily for the adjustment of the student. After months of this instruction, Bikram would let the potential new teacher start teaching.

In the early trainings, Bikram had each trainee get up and do the postures. He explained what to look for in the body and how to see what the body could do. He would explain to the other trainees what was going on in the body: what it could do, what it couldn't do, even how long it would take for the body to change. Although Bikram had been using this dialogue for a long time, there was no formal Dialogue given to the teachers yet.

As the trainings got larger, Bikram emphasized the use of his verbal Dialogue to teach a class and the use of Dialogue to correct students. This is the methodology teachers have been trained with for years and it works very well, but it requires knowing your Dialogue and learning to see the body (from the front of the room). The current training does not teach hands-on corrections, and it is not part of the philosophy of Bikram Yoga. For some students, this is the reason they come to Bikram Yoga. They do not want to be touched and/or they feel uncomfortable when teachers walk around the room.

We became teachers because we want to help people, and it can be frustrating when we feel we can't help; however, physical corrections—going over and touching students—often come as a result of the teacher's frustration. Don't let your frustration become the students' problem. You never know what's going on with them physically, emotionally, or spiritually. Touching a student can push them to a place they are not ready to go—all due to your frustration as a new teacher or just being new to making good corrections. There will be frustration, but that's your struggle.

It's not easy to learn to use words to correct, but ultimately, this tool will lead you to become a better teacher and give you space to work with students with injuries and serious limitations. The skills you add now allow you to continue to grow as a teacher for many years to come.

You might think, "I'm using Dialogue and they don't understand. I don't have a way to explain this to the students." Don't explain. You don't have to have all the answers. Don't assume you are the reason they are not doing the posture correctly. How long did you practice and you still heard new things in class? Or instructions you did not know or hear until you learned the Dialogue?

There are many reasons why a student cannot do what you are telling them to do. Perhaps they are not ready or the correction is not clear. Very often, they simply did not hear you. You may not understand all the reasons why a student cannot integrate a correction, but you don't have to. It's their job to stand on their mat and struggle. It's your job to give students information and tools and let them struggle, and it's your job to deal with your frustration and learn to let it go. Remember, the body is the body, but frustration is a choice, for teachers and students. We use our toolbox to build a better class; students use the tools we give them to build a better life.

Never Take Away a Student's Success

Sometimes, when the students are working toward the next step of a posture, they can lose some of the alignment (technique). They are often working at the edge of their range of motion. For example, they start to bring their head down in Standing Head to Knee and the kicking leg bends. You can let them struggle with the next step. You don't have to correct it. In other words, let them have their success, even if it's not 100 percent perfect. Don't take away their feeling of moving forward.

Choosing When Not to Correct

There is a skill to learning when not to correct. As a new teacher, you are not able to make corrections right away because you can't yet. You don't have the tools—you can't see what needs correcting, and you can't leave the Dialogue and come back efficiently. When you start making corrections, you go through a phase where you want to correct everything. Over time, you can learn to use corrections judiciously and learn the art of not correcting. You start to see things in the room and choose not to correct them.

Just like the practice, over time you start to figure out that sometimes less is more. Give your students the Dialogue, without a lot of corrections, and they learn to get there on their own. What they learn on that journey is the important part. This is a tool that can take a lot of time to develop, letting go of their struggle and enjoying their success. This skill, knowing what to let go of, is one of the things that will make you an amazing teacher. It's okay not to correct.

Looking for Corrections

At first, you will see things you want to correct. Then you have to learn the Dialogue to make the appropriate corrections. When you have these tools, then you can start to look for what you want to correct. You can start looking at the bodies in a whole new way—not just seeing a mistake a student is making and fixing it, but seeing how a technical correction to the body will allow more depth or benefit from the posture.

This is why you learn to correct technique, not the depth of a posture. Now you can teach technique to help the body become stronger, more flexible, and the technique-based information you give the student changes their relationship with their own body. Giving technique to change the body and then improving the technique as the body changes creates even more changes. Students keep growing, changing, and coming back because there is always more to learn.

Chapter 4
Energetic Conversation

Observe Your Self

Each student who comes into the room has their own energy. Each teacher also has their own energy and how they deal with the room of people energetically. It's an idiosyncratic thing, so to tell you how to teach energetically is nearly impossible.

I can tell you what I do, what I have seen others do, what is successful, where people make common mistakes, but ultimately, you have to figure it out for yourself. It's like trying to see the picture from inside the frame. In the room, as you're teaching, you might not know what you are doing energetically. However, you may be able to identify with some of the things described in this chapter, thereby becoming more self aware, more able to observe yourself while teaching and understanding what you do and why you do it.

> "The spine is the source of all energy in human life."
>
> – Bishnu Ghosh

Teachers use energy in many ways. In this chapter I describe from my experience. There may be many other tools of which I am unaware. This chapter is a start, a place to build common ground, to create a vocabulary we can use. This is the beginning—but far from the end—of the concept I call the "Energetic Conversation."

Collective Energy

In every class we do the same postures in the same order with the same directions; however, the class is never the same, because each day the students are different. The energy of each class is different. Each student has their individual energy, the energy they bring to their own mat.

I think it's important to greet students as they come in the door. Even there you can get a sense of where they are energetically. You can see if new students are nervous, apprehensive, or excited. And you can sense any changes in the energy of regular students you are already familiar with. When students enter the yoga room, that energy can shift. Some will relax in the room, seeing faces they know, knowing they can let go in class. Others might become tense if the room is quiet and that is overwhelming to them. The teacher adds another energetic layer.

Where students choose to stand is interesting. Some tend to practice next to someone they know and have a connection with; others will separate, even though they come to class together. I know the class will come together collectively, so I don't shift the room or move students around in class. Sometimes I might need to separate new students standing close together. But only enough to make it hard for them to whisper to each other. I find it's best for parents to stand away from their children, mainly so the parent can have a practice without worrying about the child. That being said, try to connect with the room as it is. Learn to feel the collective energy as well as the individual energy of each student.

Each class has a collective energy. Each student on their mat and the energy between the mats create that collective energy. Have you ever had a great class because of the student next to you? That sharing of energy—it can get you through the postures and the class. That is the collective energy. This is why walking around while teaching can be counter-productive; it breaks or interrupts the collective energy of the group.

Learn to teach and see the room from the front. Then you can start to feel every shift of energy in the room. As the teacher, you will lead the class with your words and energetically at the same time. When you physically move around the room, you might feel like you are moving the energy of the room but you are not moving the students' energy, you are just moving your energy around the room. You want to be able to control how energy moves and is used in the room, so stand in the front. Don't let it scare you. This energetic conversation truly starts when you stand on the podium.

To master the energy of the room, to have control of it, deciding where it goes and how to use it, you must be at the front of the room. It's the reason Bikram never leaves the podium. He is the master of controlling the energy, being in tune with it.

Energetic Conversation

Using "Your All Three Ears"

As you begin class, just observe the energy. It's where we start (and we start where we start, always). The conversation begins with breathing: "Inhale, head down, exhale, head up." This is your first chance to listen and to observe the energy.

What does that energy sounds like? In your ears, but also in your body, in the room. Inhale and exhale, just a conversation. Talk, and then listen. Feel the room. Is there a lot of energy in one part of the room? Is the energy high or low? Are students together or scattered? Sometimes, almost right away, students are energetically connected, but often at the very start of class they need time to come together. "Wait for me, please," is a way to connect them to you and them to each other—to create a collective energy of the class, which you lead.

In Pranayama Breathing, try to let go of everything you might have brought into the room with you, such as distractions or your ego. Experience the students in the room as a class. Try to look at and listen to each student. Let them build the collective energy of the room. Is the energy high or low? Connected or disjointed? Is there a place the energy is "off"? Is there a student creating a reaction in you? What is it and why? How do you want to handle that? How do you want to approach the room? All this in the first ten minutes of class. By the end of the second set of Pranayama Breathing, you have a foundation to start the conversation with the group of students in any class.

The Dialogue gives you a script to say without having to think about what you're saying, so you can have this energetic conversation. It's about listening, not talking. You have to learn to listen and be okay with whatever the energy is. Sometimes a room has a lot of energy, sometimes it doesn't. It's good to be able to increase or decrease the energy, but you don't have to make a decision about what the energy should be. Some classes are high energy, some classes can be low energy. There's no judgment attached to that; it's just what it is. It's not your class, it's their practice.

You have to learn to teach the room you're in. All types of classes are fine. All classes don't have to be high energy. It's okay to teach a low energy class. Late night, early morning, mid-day with a lot of students can all be different. You can teach a calm class that leaves them focused, and perhaps at night, ready to relax and go home to bed. Or you might bring the energy up to get the group going. These techniques take practice and patience.

Follow the Spine

There is a specific flow or pattern to the energy of our class, especially in the first few postures. You hope the class has started working together in the breathing. Keeping that connectedness is how a class works together, getting a better experience as a group than each can have individually. This is where having a variety of practitioners is beneficial, even essential. The first three postures have a great flow for the energy to move through the room and interact with the students.

All energy is from the spine; therefore, the way the spine moves is the way the flow of energy moves in the room. Individually, in the Half Moon pose warm-up, students are moving right and left, but collectively the energy should be moving up the spine to the ceiling. When you can't stretch any more—all the energy is up—then we can start the posture.

The flow of Half Moon, Backward Bending, and Hands to Feet pose is easy to follow and even though the body is moving in different directions, the energy is always from the bottom of the spine up.

Following the energetic flow of Half Moon, the energy moves up the spine and through the arms and hands. As arms lead the posture to the side, the energy moving out of the arms circles around through the hips eventually moving from the hips over the left side of the body. Can you see it in the room? Can you feel it? Can you direct it? It starts with your own practice. Feel it in your own body and spine when you practice.

Class is an energetic conversation between you and the students, and the students with each other. Your job is to lead the conversation, to guide it, but not necessarily control it. This is so much fun when you get good at it.

A Room Full of Energy

In a room of students, the energy moves within the whole space, moving in the directions of the postures. Instead of directing the movement in each individual body, you can direct the flow of energy in the whole room. Students share the experience and can take and give energy as needed to work on what their body is doing. This is throughout the room between the bodies, not just one body.

You can push energy or pull energy. There are lots of ways to move it. Each teacher has their own way of interacting with it, but learning to control your interaction is how you can become a great teacher.

It's about guiding or directing the energetic conversation, but not monopolizing it. Not filling the room with your own energy. Not deciding what the conversation should be, but working back and forth with the students to be present with them in the practice and continually re-engaging in the conversation. This makes the 90-minute class easy to stay connected to. You are part of the collective energy of the class. This is another reason not to walk around the room as it interrupts the flow of the collective energy.

There are times in class you want to keep that energy moving. Sometimes you can still the energy as well (for example, Eagle and Toe Stand), learning to move the energy sometimes in large ways, sometimes in more controlled ways. Or focusing on the energy of an individual student.

I hold the energy in the room and not in my own body. Holding the energy of the class in your body can leave you exhausted when class ends, or so energized personally that you have trouble winding down.

To use the students' energy, you have to create an environment where they feel safe sharing their energy, and you have to invite them to share. Then you use their energy to teach the class. You are using the energy of the room to teach the entire class.

There are specific points in class when there are energetic shifts. The biggest shift happens when moving from the standing (warm-up) to the floor (yoga). There is a near constant flow of energy in the standing series, but as we transition to the floor there will be a change of energy in the room. This is normal.

I start this transition at Tree and Toe Stand to quiet the energy, slow it down. It is important to learn to make this transition so you do not lose the room and specifically to keep new students engaged and connected.

Talking during the Savasana is what keeps the new student with you. The regulars (the students who have learned the art of moving meditation) can meditate right through the talking. The talking, the little jokes, that's always for the newer people to keep them engaged. You keep talking, but the energy is still.

Finding Stillness in the Posture

There is movement and energy in every posture, but the goal is to find stillness within the posture, not a continuous striving for depth. The energy of your teaching should match this goal in a way that helps influence the outcome. When students move to the floor, the conversation becomes more intimate, more subtle. By now you've seen their bodies, what they can do, where their limitations are. In the actual yoga practice, you energetically guide the bodies differently. I find that I guide more individually and less as a group. The corrections become more specific and primarily have to do with the setup. It becomes more about keeping students with you and talking to the body as opposed to the brain. This is moving meditation, eventually the brain stays in Savasana, and the body does the work.

Play with the rhythm and tempo of the Dialogue to keep the energy moving. While there is a set rhythm and flow to the class, you can play with it, using the energy of your voice and breath to influence the energy and rhythm of the class. We use the same words to create a different conversation. Change the conversation, but use the same words; this is how you make the class and the Dialogue your own.

Yoga Makes You You

Teach from your personality. Every teacher, by nature, brings their own energy and personality into the room. Often we want to emulate teachers we admire and as a rule Bikram teachers "steal" liberally from each other, but ultimately you have to present yourself, your true self. This is, again, how you get students to trust you. You can lead them anywhere and they will follow you—off a cliff or maybe just lock their knee. But if you are not your authentic self, the students sense it and might be hesitant to follow your lead. You might not know exactly who your authentic self is—yet—but that's why you get in the room and practice.

When you practice with the students, they can start to see you as you really are. Therefore, always practice with integrity. This doesn't mean you have to be "perfect" or never sit down. (It's a great example to take care of yourself when needed.) If you tell students to bend their knees going into Hands to Feet pose, then you should bend your knees when you practice. Practice what you teach; this is practicing with integrity. When the true self of your practice is in line with the true self of your teaching, you get students to work hard for you, and they really will follow you anywhere.

There is one Dialogue, and we use the same words, but every teacher is different. What makes one teacher's class speak to any individual student is the teacher's personality and energy. If you are by nature a calm and serious person, teach that class. If you are funny, teach that class. The one thing Bikram's class always has is his personality. There are times when a teacher tries to teach in a way that is not true to who they are. Perhaps they are trying to teach the studio owner's class or emulate a teacher they admire. That's fine when you can take what speaks to you and use it, but if something feels out of sorts, doesn't match who you are, then that is a tool that doesn't need to be in your toolbox. There are so many great teachers in our community, so go take a lot of different classes and learn from them, but be who you are.

Moving Energy

The energy in the room can be overwhelming for new teachers, and they may place an energetic wall between themselves and the students. If you find yourself doing this, you might feel disconnected from the class and have a hard time getting the students to move with you. Like trying to dance with someone in another room. Typically, this is actually a good sign, because it means you can feel the students' energy; you just have to learn what to do with it.

Some teachers go into the room and fill it with their energy, thinking that creates the conversation in the room. Then they try to pull their energy back and the room feels flat. In response, they give more of their energy. The problem is they haven't given the students space to bring their energy to the practice. This leaves the teacher exhausted. Remember, class is an energetic conversation, you have to leave room for both sides to contribute.

Other teachers can only move energy in the small space in front of them. This leaves the students in front of the teacher spent and students farther away feeling disconnected. To avoid this, you need to learn how to work with the energy through the whole room to give all your students flow in the class. Sometimes you can direct energy to one student more than the others to help them through a posture (careful not to decide their journey). It's a support; try not to slam them.

Many teachers attempt to get students to move together, physically synchronized, but in a room of students of different sizes and abilities, that's difficult. Instead, think of the class moving energetically together, each student sharing their own energy with the room—sometimes taking energy, sometimes giving more.

Your goal is to teach with more of the students' energy and less of your own because that's more efficient. It's a conversation, so you can't come with nothing to contribute, but you also can't create a one-sided conversation. (That's a monologue.) It needs to be a back and forth. You give some energy, and they return it. You get to use the energy they have brought to class and teach with it. But to start, it's just a simple back and forth. In learning this technique, you don't have to change the energy, just get used to feeling it, especially if you have been blocking out the students' energy or filling the room with your own. This will take some time.

If you are using the energy provided by the students, it doesn't matter what is going on in your life. If you're happy or sad, your energy does not fill the class and influence the students. You also don't feel drained at the end of class. The students get to influence the class; they dictate the energy, so you can teach a good class no matter what.

Chapter 5
About the Postures

Keep It Simple

This chapter is designed to help you understand what you are teaching— to connect the Dialogue to what is happening in the body. Have your Dialogue handy as you read this chapter.

> "What does my Dialogue say?"
>
> – Bikram Choudhury

There are some basic concepts you should understand. The main goal of teaching a class is to teach asana (the actual postures). This is a means to an end, the way to help students learn the skills to have a better life.

Don't teach the students what you know; instead, tell them what to do, how to do it, and the effect of doing it. Bring your knowledge and wisdom to the room. Be confident in the words of the moving meditation. Remember, you teach beginners in a beginner yoga class. The information they need is simple.

Trying the Right Way

In practice, trying the right way means working the sequence of the posture, in proper alignment, and without pain, through the body's full range of motion—even if that range is limited—and then holding the posture in stillness. Over time, this creates more range of motion. In teaching, trying the right way means working with the individual student's range of motion without modifying the posture. It might be necessary to modify the depth: doing less to get more benefit. When looking at your students, remember to encourage them and compliment them when they are trying the right way, even if they are only doing the first few steps of the posture.

The postures in the series work synergistically to create the overall effect of the yoga practice—not just the immediate effect students feel after taking class, but also the long-term healing effects of a consistent practice. Therefore, all the postures are important.

That being said, if a student skips a posture or two on any given day due to an acute injury or needing to rest, it does not affect the outcome of that class. However, if the series of postures is not followed properly on a long-term basis, the student will not receive the full benefit of the practice. There are times when a particular student needs to skip a posture temporarily, as the risk outweighs the benefit. Your goal is to start to move the student in the direction of the posture, allowing the posture to do its job. As the student starts to develop more range of motion, they are able to create more depth in the posture.

Every posture gets the body ready for the next posture. These are beginner postures—all students are beginners in class. The goal of the posture is to try the right way. It's not about depth or how a posture looks, it's about technique and precision. This is why we can have different levels of students in each class together, everyone doing just what they can.

Postures use leverage, using strength to build flexibility. Flexible students build strength by holding the posture in beginner technique. There is a final expression of each beginner posture, and when students achieve it, they should enjoy it, find stillness, and meditate. They can then work on the other postures in the series. The goal is not to get students into advanced postures in the beginner class. The discipline of the class is built into trying the right way, the beginner way.

The Dialogue (though grammatically incorrect in places) is unambiguous and straightforward. However, there are a few places teachers can benefit from further explanation. Once you understand these concepts, you will understand the Dialogue better, and you will become more confident in your teaching.

The Six Directions

The yoga room has six directions that are referenced in the Dialogue. It is important to understand these directions as teachers, since there is sometimes confusion. This seems simple and it is simple—but like the yoga, it is not always easy. The six directions are: Up, Down, Forward, Back, Right, and Left.

The Six Directions of the Room

Understanding the six directions will help you understand the Dialogue.

Direction	Example
UP – toward the ceiling	"Stretch UP right and left"
DOWN – toward the floor	"Pull your elbows DOWN"
FORWARD – toward the mirror, front of the room	"Hips more FORWARD" "Charge your body FORWARD"
BACK – toward the wall behind the students	"Lean BACK, fall BACK, way BACK" "Go BACK half way, and stop in the middle"
RIGHT and LEFT	"Don't mix them up"

For many teachers, reviewing these directions creates that "Aha moment" when they realize how to do the postures. For example, Stretch **up** (not side-to-side) in the Half Moon pose warm-up (when you can't stretch any more, please stop in the middle), or reach **back** (not down) in Backward Bending pose.

Understanding Pressure

The postures work by creating pressure on the body—pressure on the joints, the veins and arteries (known as the "tourniquet effect"), the organs, and the glands. The postures are designed to work the various parts of the body systematically by creating pressure and working range of motion.

When students work too hard, putting undue pressure on a joint, they lose the alignment of the posture. When a joint can't take the pressure placed on it, it tries to send the extra pressure somewhere else—to another joint—to share the load. For example, in Half Moon pose, too much pressure on the spine can cause the hip to go back and the shoulder to come forward.

When you look at a body and see that something is out of alignment, try to identify the area where there is too much pressure and the place it should be instead. The student usually has to do less, create less pressure, to bring the body back into alignment. For the flexible body, the student might need to use more strength to support the skeletal system, but always in proper alignment.

Spine-Straight Position

Everyone's anatomy is a bit different—so what does "spine-straight position" mean? Stand up tall, the way that would make your grandmother proud. The skeleton aligns so the shoulders are over the hips; the spine has a curve at the lower back and neck (the lumbar and cervical spine). Try standing like this with your back against a wall. Your hips and head touch the wall; however, there is a gap at the lower back. This is spine-straight position—when you stand up straight, keeping the natural curvature of the spine. The straight spine you use in Pranayama Breathing is the same straight spine mentioned throughout the Dialogue.

Locking the Knee

There are two reasons for locking the knee in class: full extension of the hamstring and lateral stability of the knee joint. Locking the knee has little to do with the knee and more to do with the thigh muscles. The mechanics of locking the knee are actually simple: Push your knee back through its full range of motion; contract the thigh muscles—all the way up to the hip joint; and distribute the weight all over the foot, equally, the same.

Contracting the thigh muscles causes the hamstrings to fully extend, which creates stability of the knee joint front-to-back. It also extends the ligaments on either side of the knee—keeping the knee supported side-to-side. This stability is important for balance when standing on one foot. Distributing the weight evenly on the foot ensures the ankle joint and hip joint are aligned.

Everyone's knee will look different. Students with long ligaments (a flexible knee) may have a knee that bows backwards. Students with short ligaments (especially ones who have had knee surgery) may have a knee that appears bent but is actually pushed back through its full range of motion. The position of the knee does not matter as long as all the other criteria for a locked knee are met: the knee is at its full range of motion, the weight is even on the foot (hip and ankle are aligned), and the thigh muscle is contracted.

Lock the Knee

There are two reasons why we lock the knee:
• Full extension of the hamstring
• Lateral stability of the knee joint

You might have heard you should not lock your knees when exercising. It is important to understand that in Bikram Yoga, we lock the knee in a static position. We do not move the leg while balancing on it. We use the muscles of the leg to create strength and flexibility.

Tourniquet Effect

The effect on blood flow in the postures created by compression or extension of veins and arteries is known as the tourniquet effect. Teachers often describe the tourniquet effect as "cutting off the blood supply." While this is a simple way to say it, it is not a completely accurate description of what is happening in the body.

The compression and extension of various parts of the body affect the blood flow, increasing blood pressure in one part of the body and decreasing the pressure in another part of the body. This pressure and the subsequent release—letting the pressure return to normal—create a flushing effect as the higher-pressure blood goes to the area of lower pressure. This flush brings nutrient-rich blood to the organs, ligaments, tendons, and muscles.

Breathing Normal

Bikram was once asked at a seminar, "What does breathing normal mean?" His answer was, "Close your mouth and breathe any way you can."

The goal of breathing normal is to keep the nervous system calm even when there is stress on the body. It is one of the most important skills students learn to improve the quality of their lives. Learning to keep the nervous system calm, even when there is stress, reduces the long-term negative effects of stress on the body.

Learning to control the breathing is everyone's key to a successful class. While there are several breathing cues associated with certain postures, breathing normal is learning how to control the nervous system as opposed to the nervous system controlling us.

Just tell students to breathe any way they can, mouth closed. As Bikram says, "Anything you're thinking about is probably not normal." How true!

Chapter 6
Injuries and Limitations

A Healing Hot Yoga for Every Body

Bikram Yoga is a healing yoga. It was designed to heal the body, the mind, and the spirit. Due to the nature of this practice and how well it works, it attracts students with physical limitations. Since you have already learned the skills to teach a variety of bodies (flexible and inflexible), you already have all the skills you need to teach anyone who takes your class. When dealing with a student with an injury, knowing the sequencing of the posture is essential for figuring out (step-by-step) how to get the student into the posture to their full range of motion.

> "We start with the assumption that as long as you are breathing, there is more right with you than wrong."
>
> – Jon Kabat-Zinn

The goal for all students, in any posture, is to work their full range of motion, without pain, and then try to hold it for the duration of the posture. Over time, this is what creates more range of motion and the strength to support it. The simple philosophy of "Try the Right Way" is what makes all the healing happen. Once you understand the philosophy that range of motion creates the benefit, you can help any student who takes your class—regardless of any limitation. First step, as always: don't be scared. The first time you teach a student with limitations, observe them and have no expectations. See where they are and then decide how to get them to the next step. This is often a long-term process, and all teachers at the studio need to work together to help this student. Let the student teach you what they can do.

The First Three Postures

The first three postures allow the teacher to observe students as they demonstrate the range of motion of their major joints. Half Moon, Backward Bending, and Hands to Feet pose show the full range of motion of the spine. Awkward pose shows the range of motion in the hips, knees, and ankles. Eagle pose shows the range of motion in the shoulders, elbows, wrists, hips, knees, and ankles. Once you have observed that a student has a limitation to their range of motion in these three postures, you know to pay closer attention to that student when subsequent postures work the same area of the body again.

For example, a student who cannot sit all the way down in the third part of Awkward pose has shown you they have a limitation in the knee and/or ankle. When you then teach Fixed Firm pose and other kneeling postures, you should watch this student to help them get the most benefit out of the posture by encouraging them to do as much as they can without losing alignment. Help them to modify the depth–not the technique–of the posture to achieve maximum benefit.

Approach students with curiosity and no expectations. What part of the body is causing a problem? Is the issue acute or chronic? Do the benefits of moving forward outweigh the risk? Finally, what can the students do without changing the technique of the posture and without creating pain?

If the student can't do the first step of a posture, your goal is to find a way to get them to do that first step. Don't bypass it. Whatever changes you make, modify the depth of the posture, not the technique, based on what the students' body can do, always moving in the direction of the next step. How is what you're asking them to do getting them closer to being in the posture? How is that helping them get to the next step? Observe them and focus on what they can do, the right way.

It is important to be mindful of the directions you give in class. Be careful not to add or take away information from the Dialogue, or you may inadvertently make the practice inaccessible to the students who need it the most. Even very small changes to the Dialogue can make a posture inaccessible to a student.

Many teachers tell me they don't need to focus on injured students because these students are not practicing at their studio. The truth is injured students are not practicing there because the practice is presented in a way that leaves them feeling unsuccessful. The students start to believe this yoga is not for them. Bikram Yoga is exactly the yoga they need, but it is being taught in a way that excludes students from class. It perpetuates the myth that Bikram Yoga is for people who are already in shape, not for the beginners it was designed to heal. Never take away a student's right to heal. The Dialogue provides all the tools you and the students need to be successful—especially bodies with injuries or limitations.

Trust

Before you can help any students, they have to trust you. When students trust you, you can ask them to do almost anything. It's easy for students to trust you when you stand at the front of the room and teach with confidence. The use of the Dialogue and the building of your own confidence are a great start to earning students' trust.

Creating a trusting, cooperative relationship is the first step to helping all students, but it is essential for students with injuries or limitations. The Dialogue is a moving meditation, and knowing when a posture ends and choosing to stay in the posture is part of that meditation. This is also a way for students to trust you, making it easier to stay with you. There are philosophies about not letting students predict when a posture ends, so students can stay in the moment, but this does not build trust. Knowing when the posture is going to end builds trust. When you know your Dialogue and the students trust you, you have the foundation to help students.

Pain

As with any healing modality: first, do no harm. This is a healing yoga, and pain is not a healing sensation. Students with injuries/limitations should always err on the side of doing less. In doing less, they usually get more benefit.

Pain is not a healing sensation; it is a gift. Pain is the body telling us something important. There is a difference between pain and discomfort and that is the breath. If a student is working hard but breathing normally, that's discomfort. Intense stretching, deep compression—these sensations are fine. If they can no longer breathe normally, or they're holding their breath, that's not normal. We can often see when a student is struggling with physical pain. However, never discount when they are struggling to do a posture, that they might also have emotional or spiritual pain that prevents them from going further.

Students with injuries might need to be reminded not to cause themselves pain in the practice. People living with chronic problems are often so used to living with pain they might have a hard time delineating between the sensations of stretching, compression, and actual pain. Focusing on breathing normally will help these students connect with their own bodies.

Students who don't have a good mind/body connection (either because they have lived in pain or because they have disconnected in some way) tend to push themselves too hard. Because pain is something they live with constantly, they may push themselves to the point of pain without realizing it. It's your job as a teacher to see those signs in their practice—such as pained expressions, wincing, grimacing, grunting, holding their breath, and withdrawing. Encourage them to do less so they can understand when their body is telling them to stop. **In class we create a mind/body connection, but if the mind ignores the message the body is sending, there is no real relationship.**

Often students dealing with physical pain will want to take pain relievers before class. Pain relievers may allow them to do more than they should, because they don't have the feedback from the body to stop before creating pain. This pushing past the body's natural limitation can impede the healing process. Pain relievers prevent students from having a true mind/body experience in class. The goal is not for them to do more; the goal is for them to do as much as they can without creating pain by listening to their body. This is what will improve their quality of life outside the room. For students taking pain medication, I recommend adjusting their schedule so they take their medication after class instead of before class.

Acute Injury vs. Chronic Illness

It is important to understand the differences between an acute injury, chronic illness, and more permanent disabilities. The approach is different in each case.

Injuries usually have a component of pain and inflammation. Pain is designed to prevent further injury, and inflammation starts the healing process by limiting mobility. The body reacts to acute injury by creating inflammation. That inflammation must be allowed to subside before you can create too much pressure in that part of the body; otherwise, you're just creating more inflammation. Students should continue to be cautious and judicious, allowing time for the pain and inflammation to subside. Students (and teachers) need to be patient to allow true healing to begin.

An acute injury is a recent injury or issue. It could be a surgical procedure, a fall, or throwing out the back. An acute injury typically presents with pain and inflammation. Sometimes this student just needs to come in the room and rest or do gentle stretching.* You never want a student with an acute issue to push at any point. This student is not working on any depth of posture. Their only focus should be to move through their full range of motion, even if that is very limited, without pain, letting the heat and increased circulation help with the healing process.

A chronic illness can present in a myriad of ways. Bikram Yoga is designed to help heal chronic problems. Again, this is done by working the range of motion, focusing on technique and alignment to create greater range of motion and depth. Chronic injuries benefit from stretching scar tissue, increasing circulation to the area, and improving range of motion. When you work with students trying to heal chronic problems, remember the goal of the practice is to improve the quality of life outside the room. The focus is never on what the postures look like in class.

Building a relationship with these students and finding out what their goals are outside yoga can help you gauge their success. For example, a student with chronic shoulder problems might want to start golfing again or playing other sports. Someone with chronic back pain might want to improve the quality of their sleep (or start having sex again). These are the milestones to strive for without regard for what they are able to do in class. The practice is a means to an end.

When the risk outweighs the benefit, don't do the posture. **Doing something is not always better than doing nothing, but doing nothing is always better than doing something wrong.** Sometimes doing nothing is the hardest thing to do. It's okay, as a teacher, not to have all the answers. You can learn to let the students' body teach you what it needs. The greatest teachers you'll ever have in the room are your students. Let them teach you.

Savasana is a legitimate posture at any point in class. You, as the teacher, may have to encourage a student with an acute injury to rest and be in savasana. Some students can benefit from just being in the heat and resting. Students need to know they can rest and do nothing if that's what they need to do. Again, doing something is not always better than doing nothing.

---

*When students show up with an acute injury, I often tell them "That's okay, take it easy. You're just doing 'gentle stretching' today." This is a great way to remind them that their goal is to take care of themselves so they can heal as quickly as possible. ✒

If the studio has rules or a culture that doesn't support students when they need to rest, injured students stay away from class when they need it the most. The acute injury may become chronic before these students return to class. In general, it is easier to heal an acute injury before it becomes a chronic problem. New injuries or problems require the teacher to support the student by asking very little of their practice and encouraging them to take care of themselves.

Other Limitations

Students who have more permanent limitations might require more assistance. For example, students with amputations, blindness, deafness, or conditions that require them to use a wheelchair or that keep them from standing unaided might require hands-on help, a chair, or other props.

Every student is an individual, so approach each one in a way that suits their individual needs. At first it's best to watch them and let them show you what they are able to do. Don't look for a modification to a posture, even for students with limitations. These students must be allowed to struggle like everyone else. Never underestimate what they are capable of doing. The challenges these students are dealing with in class might be new to you; however, they have learned to live with these challenges daily and often have ways to adapt. Let students struggle using their own body before using props.

While there are as many challenges as there are students, there are some problems that present more commonly. The following sections explain some approaches to these specific problems.

Knee Issues

Students show up with a variety of knee problems including surgeries, replacements, and injuries. When approaching these students, there are two questions you need answered: Does it hurt to bend the knee (compression of the knee joint)? Does the pressure of the floor against the knee cause pain? If compression is the problem, the student will have trouble sitting on their heels. Students start by kneeling on all fours and bringing the hips as close to the heels as possible, never creating any pain. This is sitting down Japanese style for this student. If pressure of the floor against the knee is creating pain, the student can roll or double up their mat and/or towel to create some cushion.

Some of the tools you implement to help a student will depend on what you see when they do the first three postures. When you see a student with knee issues in the first three postures, be sure to watch this student in Tree pose and Toe Stand as well as all the kneeling postures (Fixed Firm, Half Tortoise, Camel, and Rabbit).

There is no instruction to lock the knees in Pranayama Breathing or Half Moon pose. Particularly for students with knee problems, locking the knees in these postures can cause knee pain which might last the entire class. In the first part of Awkward pose, make sure their weight is in the heels and the hips are going back (towards the back wall). A student who cannot sit on their heels in the third part of Awkward pose should only go as far as they can without bringing the upper body forward. When the body leans forward, it puts pressure on the knees.

> "You can mess with the Gods,
> but you don't with your knees."
> – Bikram Choudhury

As with any student, you want those with knee issues to work through full range of motion even if that range is limited. Let them struggle to get the foot in Standing Head to Knee pose and in Standing Bow Pulling pose. Let them just do the best they can, one step at a time.

Once on the floor, students who cannot fully compress the knee can benefit from a few helpful techniques:
- For the student who is struggling to grab their foot in Bow pose, they can bring their knee out to the side, grab the foot, and then bring the knee back behind them. If they are not able to get both feet, they can do one foot at a time (one first set, the other second set). Always encourage the students to keep reaching for the other foot during the posture.
- In Fixed Firm pose, the student can kneel on all fours and try to bring the hips to the heels. This is what will give them more range of motion over time. They can use some cushioning under the knee, if needed. This kneeling on all fours position can also become the starting position for Half Tortoise and Rabbit pose. In Half Tortoise pose, walk the hands forward to get into the posture.

- In Rabbit pose, students can put their hands next to their knees to go down. Bring the head in as close to the knees as possible and on the floor, then grab the heels. Time is the key to healing knees. No strain, no pain! Working full range of motion and breathing normal at all times. Again, doing less gives the student more benefit.

Back Issues

Students suffering from back pain (for example, herniated discs, bulging discs, or strain) need to be careful when forward bending, even skipping the forward bending postures completely—especially for acute herniation. Forward bending allows the disc to push out of alignment. This is why people who have "thrown their backs out" have usually done so by leaning forward, typically to pick something up off the floor. While forward bending might feel okay, it puts the back in a vulnerable position.

Backward bending, on the other hand, is healing, especially for lower back issues. It creates pressure with the vertebra on the disc, helping to move the disc back into alignment. Compression of the muscles on both sides of the spine helps to create strength to support the spine. People with acute back injuries should come to class as soon as possible. The sooner they come to class, the faster they heal.

For acute back injury, there should be no forward bending until pain is gone. Then, they can carefully start to forward bend and not induce further inflammation. You never want to irritate an acute back injury by creating pain in class, because an acute back injury can become a chronic back problem. This is the reason students need to get into the room right away when they have an acute back problem, to prevent it from becoming chronic. Be patient. The goal is to keep the disc in alignment, not to push it back out again. Make new additions to forward bending mindfully. No hurry. No pain. Students healing a back injury should also skip the sit-ups, especially the sit-up between Head To Knee and Stretching pose. That sit-up is particularly unsupported and should only be added back in once all the other forward bending postures are being performed with no pain.

Neck Issues

Students who come in with neck issues (for example, whiplash, herniation, or stiffness) might feel limited right from the beginning of class. Pranayama Breathing is stressful and difficult when there is limited motion in the neck. These students often feel defeated from the beginning, and they need tools and encouragement to feel like they are getting benefit.

The goal of Pranayama Breathing is breathing. Again, the benefit comes from moving the body through its full range of motion, even if it's limited. If students are using their full range of motion and they're breathing, they are getting the benefit of Pranayama Breathing.

In Pranayama Breathing and for the rest of class, students with neck issues should use their eyes to guide their head through the posture; where the eyes go, the body will follow. At the point where they cannot look any farther, they should stop—no pushing past this point. This is their full range of motion for now. Over time, with a consistent practice, their range of motion will increase.

Students need to understand that the standing series is simply the warm-up to get ready for the floor series. The floor series, the actual yoga of the class, will create the healing of the neck and the whole body. Students with limitations need to let go of any attachment to the postures of the standing series and focus on the yoga practice. As healing happens, the student will see greater range of motion and ability in the standing series.

Mental Illness

Bikram Yoga is very good for people with mental illness. Because we teach without wandering around the room or touching people, it is accessible for students with mental dis-ease, trauma survivors, PTSD, anxiety disorders, drug and alcohol recovery, OCD, autism, and a variety of other disorders.

Having just one thing to focus on can help quiet the mind and create a better mind/body connection, helping to maintain well being. Simply learning to breathe is helpful for many students with anxiety.

The repetitive nature of the practice allows students to know what is coming next and helps them to have clear expectations. This method allows them to feel safe in your class. Your walking around or touching a student can make other students nervous or uncomfortable, even if you are not touching them. Many students come to Bikram Yoga because of its hands-off nature.

Mental health issues can be very isolating. Having a place to go and be with others and creating a community, can help them to be more at ease in class, in their own body, and outside the room.

Some students inform teachers they have a mental health issue, but many will not. As teachers, we sometimes think we know our students, but we can never really know what they are dealing with on any given day. Often we can see that the students are dealing with something in class. With all students, having no judgment and approaching with acceptance and compassion is the best plan.

> "It should never surprise us that a yoga so good for the mentally ill attracts the mentally ill."
>
> – Jack X

Pregnancy

Rajashree Choudhury has written a book, produced a DVD, and does seminars about the safe practice of Bikram Yoga during pregnancy. The modifications that Rajashree uses are safe and effective for pregnant women and should be followed. One of the best ways to learn to teach the pregnancy series as a teacher is to practice it yourself. Rajashree's series adds in extra resting periods and allows the pregnant woman to keep her blood pressure and heart rate under control. Learning to rest is an important skill for pregnant women and new mothers.

To Sum Up

The goal for all students is to use their full range of motion. The best thing you can teach students with a limitation is to be patient and compassionate with themselves. These are skills they need outside the room, too. Patience and compassion are what allow healing to happen physically, emotionally, and spiritually.

Chapter 7
Mentoring

We Start Where We Start

After you have been teaching for a while and have spent time studying your craft you might wonder, "What's next?" Teaching is a joy when you reach this stage. While there are always new things to learn, for many teachers the next step may be to mentor another teacher. Mentoring is a special opportunity to share the tools you have with others and, even more importantly, it creates an environment in which to look at the tools you've collected and really examine what works, what doesn't, and how you developed those tools.

> "The delicate balance of mentoring someone is not creating them in your own image, but giving them the opportunity to create themselves."
>
> – Steven Spielberg

The mentor and the mentee comprise a unique relationship. The two must be able to meet in a positive place and build that relationship on respect and trust. The goal is growth for both parties. This can only happen when you create a cooperative relationship. Just as you have learned with your students in class, the cooperative relationship fosters growth and change.

It's important to understand that not everyone is a good match. Picking the right mentor or mentee is more about ourselves than the other person. Both parties must be willing to be vulnerable, to meet without judgment. As a mentee, choose a mentor whose class you want to emulate. As a mentor or mentee, look for someone whose temperament suits your own. It's important to trust your instincts. Much of this decision is intuitive; you'll probably know when it feels right (or when it feels wrong).

Any teacher looking to grow in a mentoring relationship must have two things: the will to seek mentorship and the grace to receive it. This is also true for the mentor. You don't have to be a studio owner to mentor another teacher, and you don't have to mentor teachers just because you are a studio owner. All you really need is a willingness to share the tools you've collected with another teacher.

"We start where we start." I use this phrase often, but in a mentoring relationship it's especially true. It's important to accept teachers where they are. Start with the class they are teaching now and then add tools so they can teach a better class.

First, Listen

The first time I take a class for the purpose of mentoring, I simply experience class as a student without the goal of giving feedback to the teacher. When I take class a second time, I make detailed notes on everything the mentee is doing well, noting skills they possess that are working and that can be applied in other places to improve their teaching. I also write down any mistakes I notice. I listen to hear if lines of Dialogue are missing or if the sequencing is off. I note places the teacher might be parroting information they have heard from other teachers. I write it all down. The purpose isn't to give them a list of things they are doing wrong but to see if there is a pattern to the mistakes, as is often the case. Taking notes helps to identify these patterns. Later I choose one or two items for the mentee to begin working on.

Feedback

There is an effective formula to giving feedback after you have closely observed your mentee: First, tell them what they are doing well and how to apply those skills to other parts of their class. Next, identify one or two areas that can be improved and give them a tool or tools they can use to work on those areas.

Starting with what they are doing well is how you instill confidence in teachers. The goal is always to build on success. Then find ways to apply those same skills to the rest of the class. Building teachers' confidence allows them to move from where they are currently to the next step of teaching. This also models good skills in offering encouragement to students; how you treat a mentoring teacher is how they will treat and encourage students. Constructive criticism is helpful. Criticism is not. No one grows from focusing on the negative. Be compassionate and positive.

Use your experience to help the mentee identify what to work on next. Usually, there are lots of things they might work on; however, most teachers can only work on two or three things at a time. Keep it simple. Once they have a good foundation of Dialogue and start adding in corrections, the other tools of teaching come more easily. Many teachers need a mentor to point out where their strengths lie, giving them confidence and support as they work on filling their toolbox.

There is a difference between mentoring a new teacher and a more experienced one. With new teachers, the focus isn't on adding tools, it is giving them the opportunity to work on their foundation of Dialogue. With more experienced teachers, make sure their foundation is solid and then help them start adding new tools.

Mentoring a New Teacher

Watching a new teacher return from training and begin teaching is an incredibly rewarding (and sometimes painful) experience. Some new teachers are great right out of the gate, others are not, and it is no reflection on where they will end up. I want every new teacher to receive support and mentoring from the start. Get brand new teachers on the podium and let them teach. Celebrate their first class— it is the last step of teacher training. I tell all teachers who teach their first class at my studio: When you are done, no matter what students say to you, the correct response is "Thank you." Encourage the mentee to teach one class at a time, again and again.

When I work with a brand new teacher, I start simply. Most teachers finish training and think they don't know their Dialogue, but they do. They spent nine weeks (or more) memorizing Dialogue, getting it in their heads, so for the first few classes, I just want to let them start spitting it back out. Sometimes I even take their Dialogue away. I don't want them to study (to put more in)—I want them to let it flow out.

Most new teachers cannot integrate feedback right away. They need many classes to get the words they've memorized to start to flow out. Giving them more to think about doesn't help this process. First classes are just that: beginner classes. I rarely give feedback on a first class. I just tell them to come back tomorrow, and we'll do it again.

As a mentor, listen in class for any wrong information. Not just a simple mistake, but information that is incorrect or directions that are actually wrong. This is the main concern for the first 25 classes or so, until the new teacher is consistently saying the correct directions and information over and over. In the beginning, I focus on weeding out incorrect information from their dialogue, and I only give feedback on things they say that are wrong (usually information they heard from other teachers, or just a misunderstanding of the posture).

The next step is to fill in any missing directions or sequencing issues. Your job is to help them understand why we say what we say and how the Dialogue works. Build their confidence and help them hone precise Dialogue. It can take a long time to get the Dialogue down, to have all the directions in the right order. Be patient while they keep working on it.

Often the first thing I ask new teachers to do is learn the Dialogue for the sit-up. We say it over and over in class, it's easy to learn, and it provides an instant success. From there, I focus on a posture where their Dialogue is very close, setting them up for another success and building on that.

The Dialogue has the timing of the postures and the class built in. If you teach a straight Dialogue class, you should be spot on with the timing (90 minutes). It can take a new teacher several classes before that timing settles in. New teachers' classes tend to run short, which means they need to keep working on adding missing Dialogue.

Some new teachers can deliver great Dialogue from the very beginning, but often those teachers can't really see what's happening in the room—it's almost as if they are reading the Dialogue in their head. Conversely, some new teachers can see the room from the very beginning, and often this leads them to struggle with the Dialogue—they can't focus on two things at once. Until a teacher can see the room and say the Dialogue at the same time, they aren't ready to add any more tools.

Until the new teacher has a solid foundation, all the other things can wait. Don't rush this process. The skills new teachers put in place by building a good foundation are the skills that will serve them as they add to their toolbox.

Just like the students' first class, the first time a teacher receives feedback can set the tone for their entire teaching career. When the first experience with feedback and mentoring is positive, new teachers will find feedback a positive and welcome experience. However, if their first experience is negative, it may undermine their power and confidence, and they may become resistant to receiving feedback altogether. When you work with a new teacher, set them up for a good future. Give them tools for success.

Mentoring an Experienced Teacher

With experience, the Dialogue transforms from being something we simply recite to an essential tool we rely on to teach a solid class. When I work with someone who has been teaching a while, I still want to see what that foundation looks like, but I also want to see if they understand what the Dialogue means. If this teacher does not have a foundation of good Dialogue, they should work on that first.

A strong understanding of how the words work with the body becomes the powerful tool that allows an experienced teacher to add new tools and skills to their teaching.

Identify other tools the teacher has developed—making corrections, energy in the room, and working with different body types and learners. The goal is to add to the tools the experienced teacher is already using.

These teachers may need techniques to streamline their class and to find their own voice in the Dialogue. They may need guidance to take the tools and use them more effectively to teach the room. They may have to work through how to make decisions in the room, while keeping the class moving. As a mentor, you can share your experience in these areas to help the teacher become better.

When taking classes to give feedback to an experienced teacher, write down everything you think they are doing well. Then look at the tools discussed in this book (such as corrections and energy) and help them focus on what's next in their teaching. Give them concrete things to work on and ways to work on them.

Share any tools you've developed. Don't be attached to the outcome; the goal is to give the teacher tools to add to their toolbox. Ultimately, they decide which tools to use—what works best for them.

One approach I employ when mentoring teachers is to have them observe a class. While teachers might take our class often, watching class and taking notes is a different experience. By observing, they can see what we see, how we make corrections (or choose not to correct), and how we interact with the room. All this opens the door to a conversation about the teaching process.

Based on the mentee's comments, notes and questions, I can begin to see what they are focused on, where they are looking to grow or perhaps feeling stuck. Knowing where teachers are helps me see what they are interested in learning and where we can start.

A good mentoring relationship can last for years—even entire teaching careers. Both parties continue to share and to grow as they go. The goal for both is to never stop improving.

Chapter 8
Teach from Love

Lifetime Practice

The goal of a yoga practice is to feel better outside the room, to have a better quality of life. In other words, we do yoga to be better, not at yoga, but at life. This powerful yoga, when practiced consistently, allows practitioners to have a better quality lifestyle because they learn to love and accept themselves.

When taught properly, Bikram Yoga is a sustainable lifetime practice. That means students can continue to practice well into their seventies, eighties, and even nineties, regardless of when they started. As the lives of students change—day to day and over time—so will their practice. Learning to moderate their practice to the day—the changes in their bodies, the room, the environment—is what makes the practice sustainable.

When students know this is a safe, loving place to come back to again and again, they do. We become their wellness center. When students are injured, ill, or need healing, they can practice frequently, even every day, to bring the body back to well being. When students are happy and healthy, they can practice less often. Whenever they need healing physically, emotionally, spiritually, they have a place to go.

> "Love is the ability and willingness to allow those that you care for to be what they choose for themselves, without any insistence that they satisfy you."
>
> – Wayne Dyer

That being said, taking class and working at 100% every time, every day, is not a sustainable practice. Students—and especially teachers—can get burnt out trying to sustain that.

Take Care of Yourself

Making a living as a yoga teacher is not easy financially, and this can lead to stress. Many teachers find they must teach a lot of classes to make ends meet. Teaching all those classes means having less time to practice. In that process the stress reliever that works for us (our practice) can become a stressor.

When you are teaching but not practicing, you are not maintaining the skills that allow you to stay calm under stress. Instead of reacting with the parasympathetic nervous system, your body lets the sympathetic nervous system take over. This can trigger your fight-or-flight response on the podium. You might unknowingly begin to take out this stress on the students. You may, consciously or unconsciously, begin to resent the students who have time to practice when you do not.

When you find yourself getting angry or frustrated or judging students easily, the answer is always the same: the wrong body part is facing the mirror. Get off the podium and get on your mat. Making time for your own practice can be difficult, but it makes you a better, more effective teacher. It might even mean making other life choices, such as taking a supplemental job or changing your lifestyle.

Take care of yourself and your students. Let go of any judgment of them or yourself. Then teaching can be a joy for you. As a teacher, you get to have this yoga lifestyle where your job is not really work, your practice is sustainable, and the life you live outside the room is satisfying and fulfilling.

Unconditional Love

The greatest gift you can give students is to love them unconditionally, to show them through your teaching and actions that they are loveable and deserving of love. I know it sounds simple, but it's not always easy. As I said at the beginning, my philosophy for teaching is: all students will be loved until they love themselves, and then we will love them even more.

People who love themselves treat themselves well. It's easy to take care of an individual you love. You feed them well, and you don't do anything that might harm them. Imagine a class full of people who love themselves. This is the gift you give them: the tools to take care of themselves that allow them to practice loving themselves, to look in the mirror and see who they are, to have the opportunity to align themselves with who they truly are.

I love all students unconditionally. I wish they could see themselves the way I see them. I wish they could see how wonderful they are, each of them perfect in their imperfection. Students come in with the will to change something but not always the grace to receive that change. We give them the tools they need to make those changes, one class at a time, so that when the grace arrives, they can change.

Be Great

Learning to be a great teacher takes time and commitment, but the payback is enormous. You become a confident teacher and a confident being. Teacher training is only the beginning of this journey. The great teachers I know have the same certificate that I have—and the same certificate you have. You don't need anyone's permission to be a great teacher. Your greatest asset in this is your own will to learn. I am constantly learning and growing. I learned through my own efforts, as I continued my own education, how to be a more effective, efficient teacher.

I learn new things from students every day, and everything I learn makes me a better person. The truth is I receive much more than I could ever give, and that is incredibly satisfying. My greatest teachers have always been the students standing on their mats looking to improve their lives through the practice of yoga.

What we do as teachers changes lives. Never underestimate your impact on students. You affect them in ways you will never know, simply by standing at the front of the room and helping them learn the tools to have a great life.

Teaching from love will allow you to open the door to any student who has the will to show up for class. The tools you use to teach facilitate the changes in the students with the grace to receive them. You take them as they come. Love them all, and celebrate every moment of being a teacher.

Appendix A
Don't 'Splain

When teachers go to a seminar, read a great yoga article, or learn something new, it's natural to want to share all the information with their students. Sometimes it's great information, but there are times when teachers explain things just to show what they know.

Because we have students of various levels in the same class, often the information is accessible to only a few students. The point: you can share, but long explanations take time away from class. There's no time.

> "Let me 'splain, No! There is too much... Let me sum up."
>
> – Inigo Montoya
> *The Princess Bride*

Too much explaining makes students think, taking them out of the moving meditation. For the most part, you want to keep your students moving—keeping the mind/body connection. If there is something you feel you can share: **sum it up**. Tell them in as few words as possible. Find ways to use simple, direct ways to transfer information. One or two sentences is enough—either they get it or they don't. If not, then maybe they just weren't ready.

In my experience, when a teacher is having to go on and on to explain a point about the practice—very often, they are a little bit off on what they are trying to explain.

My point? Let me sum up: be judicious with your words. The key to effective communication is brevity.

Don't 'splain, just sum it up.

Appendix B
Meet Elaine

On August 15, 2008, Elaine, at the age of 72, started practicing yoga at Bikram Yoga Merrimack Valley. She had diabetes, high cholesterol, and uncontrolled blood pressure. She was caring for her husband, who was homebound at the time. Her son and daughter both practiced Bikram Yoga, and they urged her to try a class with them. Her daughter promised, if Elaine took three classes, they would never mention yoga to her again. Elaine agreed.

At first, Elaine was able to do Pranayama Breathing, and then she would lie down for most of the class. She would prop herself up against the back wall for Blowing in Firm pose. To her surprise, Elaine felt an improvement in her health after taking just three classes. She felt better. In class, she improved slowly in increments, but always trying the right way. In time, she began a regular practice, and the students and teachers watched her make great strides in her strength, stamina, and health status. As Elaine got stronger, she practiced more and more often.

In May 2009, Elaine decided to try a Five-Day Challenge, which she successfully completed. She extended it to a 30-Day Challenge, then a 60-Day Challenge. She successfully completed both, which gave her confidence and determination. Elaine went on to complete 365 classes in 365 days! Elaine happily continued with a consistent Bikram Yoga practice. For her 75th birthday, the studio crowned her the "Official Ambassador of Bikram Yoga Merrimack Valley."

In February 2012, Elaine completed her 1,000th class in 996 days! She has maintained a consistent practice since then. Elaine takes a day off now and then, but often completes a "double" (two classes in the same day) on days when she feels she needs it for her overall well being.

Elaine loves taking classes from new teachers and watching them grow. In April 2016, our Bikram Yoga community helped her celebrate her 80th birthday! If you are ever struggling with how to teach from love, imagine you are teaching Elaine—she makes teaching from love easy.

"Most people my age get up in the morning and take pills. I get up in the morning and take yoga."

– Elaine Brophy, age 80

References

Choudhury, Bikram. *Bikram's Beginning Yoga Class*. New York: Tarcher, 1978. [Red Book]

Choudhury, Bikram. *Bikram's Beginning Yoga Class*, 2nd ed. New York: TarcherPerigee, 2000. [Blue Book]

Choudhury, Bikram. *Bikram's Beginning Yoga Class Authorized Teacher's Dialogue*. Los Angeles: Bikram's Yoga College of India, 2002.

Goldman, William. *The Princess Bride*. Film. Directed by Rob Reiner. 1987. Beverly Hills: Twentieth Century Fox Home Entertainment, 2007. DVD.

Kabat-Zinn, Jon. *Full Catastrophe Living: Using the Wisdom of Your Body and Mind to Face Stress, Pain, and Illness*. New York: Delta, 2009.

Roach, Michael, and Christie McNally. *How Yoga Works: Healing Yourself and Others with the Yoga Sutra*. Pompton Plains, NJ: Diamond Cutter Press, 2004.

Saunders, George. "George Saunders on Kindness." *Shambhala Sun*, May 2014, 37–40.

Steven Spielberg. BrainyQuote.com, Xplore Inc, 2016. http://www.brainyquote.com/quotes/quotes/s/stevenspie584069.html, accessed May 7, 2016.

Thomas A. Edison. BrainyQuote.com, Xplore Inc, 2016. http://www.brainyquote.com/quotes/quotes/t/thomasaed105328.html, accessed May 7, 2016.

Wayne Dyer. BrainyQuote.com, Xplore Inc, 2016. http://www.brainyquote.com/quotes/quotes/w/waynedyer401252.html, accessed May 7, 2016.

Testimonials

"Teri and her beautiful Teach From Love community taught me many lessons, like: Be true to yourself and make sure to always teach from your heart. I learned building blocks to becoming a strong teacher, not only in my Dialogue but also understanding my students' bodies and being able to really see them."

– Polly Edwards, Studio Owner, Bikram Yoga Luxembourg

"When I started teaching, I had very little confidence and struggled to get through every class. When the struggle became too much, I decided to quit. However, my daughter, also a Bikram Yoga teacher, told me to contact Teri before I acted on my decision. I did. She asked me to teach a class at her studio, and for the very first time, I was given positive feedback. The feeling I was actually doing something right was new for me. So I kept teaching, with Teri as my mentor. Slowly but surely, things started to turn around. Now, three years later, I'm a strong confident Dialogue teacher."

– Jeni Ogilvy, Bikram Yoga Teacher (Bedford, New Hampshire)

"Teri Almquist has a relentless passion for Bikram Yoga and a penchant for sharing this passion with everyone within her sphere of influence, student and teacher alike."

– Ben Boyle, Owner, Tranquil Point Retreat (Tasmania, Australia)

"I highly recommend Teri's book, her mentorship program, and her Teach From Love seminars to every Bikram Yoga teacher. On my journey of practicing and teaching Bikram Yoga I have never seen or experienced someone with such love and devotion for the students and detailed knowledge. Working with Teri is like taking the fast lane to becoming a mature and meaningful teacher."

– Sebastian Metcalfe, Bikram Yoga Teacher (Hamburg, Germany)

"Teri's dedication and commitment to furthering the education of new and experienced teachers around the world has been constant since she made the decision of becoming a teacher herself. Teri, please continue what you are doing—it's working!"

– Darren Stockwell, Bikram Yoga Teacher (Queensland, Australia)

About The Author

Teri Almquist has been teaching Bikram Yoga full time since 2005. She opened her studio, Bikram Yoga Merrimack Valley, in 2008. Her passion for Bikram Yoga grew out of her own healing experience: In 1991, Teri suffered a severe injury that ruptured the discs in her neck and left her unable to move her head; after years of discomfort, she discovered Bikram Yoga and in 2004 began practice as a last-ditch effort to put off seemingly inevitable spinal surgery. With patience and consistent practice, she was able to avoid surgery completely and eventually regained full, pain-free range of motion in her neck. Now teachers and students from all corners of the globe consult Teri for her expertise in healing injured bodies through Bikram Yoga. In 2015, she founded Teach From Love, an organization dedicated to the continuing education of Bikram Yoga teachers. Teri lives in Haverhill, Massachusetts, with her husband, Tom. When not in the hot room, she enjoys cooking, kayaking, playing at the beach, and talking about yoga.

teach.from.love

In 2015, Teri Almquist launched Teach From Love. Dedicated to the continuing education of certified Bikram Yoga teachers, Teach From Love offers a variety of growth opportunities for teachers:

Webinars
Teach From Love webinars make it possible to add tools to your toolbox from anywhere in the world. Join Teri, and occasional guest presenters, for a live webinar each month. View recordings of our previous webinars at: http://webinars.teachfromlove.yoga

Seminars
Seminars pack several months' worth of mentoring information into a one-week format. They include daily yoga classes, lectures on all aspects of Bikram Yoga, posture clinics focused on the anatomy of the postures, and plenty of time for relaxation and socializing with other teachers.

Workshops
Two-day workshops provide a forum for teachers to ask questions and get reinspired. Check the schedule for upcoming workshops, or schedule a workshop for Teri to come to your studio and work with your teachers.

Mentoring
Teri continues to open her home to teachers looking to grow. This is an opportunity for one-on-one interaction and personal feedback focused on your individual needs.

For more information on all of the above, see: www.teachfromlove.yoga

Teach From Love Facebook Group
If you are a certified Bikram Yoga teacher, please join our Facebook group:
https://www.facebook.com/groups/Teach.From.Love

CPSIA information can be obtained
at www.ICGtesting.com
Printed in the USA
FSOW03n1748210916
25243FS

9 780997 565706